/ п.P8

TRACK

JIM PIKE

SUTTON PUBLISHING

*To my wife Patricia, who has been
a constant source of encouragement
and help. This book is hers as much
as it is mine.*

First Published in 2001 by
Sutton Publishing Limited · Phoenix Mill
Thrupp · Stroud · Gloucestershire · GL5 2BU

Reprinted in 2002

British Library Cataloguing in Publication Data
A catalogue record for this book is available from the British Library

ISBN 0 7509 2692 9

Typeset in 10.5/13.5 Photina
Typesetting and origination by
Sutton Publishing Limited.
Printed and bound in Great Britain by
J.H. Haynes & Co. Ltd, Sparkford.

CONTENTS

INTRODUCTION

The aim of this book is to give the interested lay person an idea of the history and development of railway track. It will not make the reader an instant civil engineer, but hopefully it will answer some of the questions that an enquiring mind may ask. It is difficult to start with the first 'railway'. How far back can one go? Wooden railways, using manpower for traction, were to be found in medieval mines. Much erudite ink has been expended, in the columns of *The Railway Magazine* and elsewhere, in tracing the use of guided ways for wheels back to Ancient Rome, and of guided sledges to Ancient Babylon. Such researches are usually focused on the question of the origin of the standard gauge of 4ft 8½in. The author feels that such investigations, fascinating though they undoubtedly are, are not relevant to the task in hand, and he is content to settle for the horse-operated wooden railway as a starting point.

Since track is part and parcel of the railways' infrastructure, some space in the pages that follow is devoted to civil engineering: cuttings, embankments, bridges, tunnels. The early railway builders found that they had some novel problems to solve, and they adopted a variety of methods of approach. Not all were successful, and some structures have been replaced. But the best still stand as a memorial, not only to the vision and imagination of the engineers, but to the wielders of pick and shovel who transformed the engineers' plans and drawings into reality.

The track had to adapt with the introduction of steam locomotives, and again as the latter became heavier and train speeds became higher. A certain amount of movement under a passing train is desirable to give an easier ride, but not movement sufficient to displace the track and cause the derailment of a following train. Ballast consisting of crushed granite proved superior to shingle from beaches, although the latter was available in limitless quantities without charge. The bull-head rail has now given way to the flat-bottomed rail, and rail sections have increased in size over the years to carry heavier loads. The wooden sleeper is only now giving way to a concrete equivalent, and welded rails have removed the once familiar 'duddety-dun' of the rail joints. Electric traction has arrived, and the track has had to adapt accordingly.

My attitude to electrification of track has been somewhat ambivalent. Since third and fourth rail electrification directly affects the track, in particular its sleepers, I have tried to cover it in this book. But, since the overhead wires which are suspended from overhead gantries do not

(Opposite) Fig. 1. Straight and true. The former Midland main line to Scotland, near Keighley, 2000. *(Author)*

directly affect the track, I have, somewhat reluctantly and for reasons of space, had to omit them.

A variety of signs have been erected beside railway tracks for the information of train crews and others, and some of these are mentioned, but I have deliberately ignored signalling. Not only would it unbalance the book, but several excellent works, covering the subject with varying degrees of technicality, are already available.

Light and narrow gauge railways scarcely need a separate mention: they have used the same concept of trackwork, merely scaled down by the use of a lighter rail section and, in the case of narrow gauge lines, shorter sleepers. In these days of steam railway preservation, the Talyllyn Railway in Wales adopted the practice of purchasing second-hand sleepers from British Railways and simply cutting them in half; other lines have probably done the same. It is, perhaps, worth spending a few words on trying to define the term 'light railway'. This is difficult, because in defining the term the Light Railways Act also uses the expression; this is tantamount to saying that a light railway is a light railway! In practice, it means that a railway built and/or operated under the provisions of the Act is limited to a maximum speed of 25mph, and main line signalling standards do not apply. The result is that today it is possible to see lines like the Keighley & Worth Valley Light Railway (to give it its full title) operating trains with the biggest main line steam locomotives!

But in their heyday, from about 1890 to the 1930s, light railways generally were rural concerns working on a shoestring. Permanent way consisted of a single track of lightweight flat-bottomed rail spiked directly to the sleepers, and earth or gravel ballast. Weed control was negligible or non-existent, and the same could be said for maintenance. Train speeds were very low: anything faster than about 20mph would precipitate derailment. Such lines were easy prey for the motor bus and lorry. The survivors have turned to the leisure market, offering a 'steam train' experience. The goods trains carrying agricultural produce, once so typical of lines such as the Welshpool & Llanfair and the Kent & East Sussex, are now but a distant memory – or a photographers' special. The preserved lines maintain their track to a vastly higher standard than the old-time 'light railway'. Heavier rails with more sophisticated fastenings, ex-British Rail spent (and cleaned) crushed granite ballast, oiled and well-adjusted rail joints, all betoken a keen awareness of safety criteria. They are also a sign of the financial resources of a supporters' club such as pre-war light railway managements could only envisage in their wildest dreams. The down side is that many preserved lines are truncated. The West Somerset runs from Minehead to Bishops Lideard and does not (yet) reach Taunton; the Yorkshire Dales Railway runs from Embsay to Bolton Abbey, and does not (yet) reach Skipton. Even the Talyllyn runs from Tywyn to Nant Gwernol, a point on the map well suited to the rambler and offering beautiful views but not much else to other passengers. It has been said of such lines that they run from Somewhere to the Middle of Nowhere. For the passengers of such lines, it is much better to travel hopefully than to arrive!

> Your author's wife, when a volunteer worker on the Talyllyn Railway, well remembers the lady who asked her if there was a Woolworth's at Nant Gwernol!

ONE

EARLY RAILWAYS

he origins of trackwork are, obviously, the origins of railways. Just what constitutes a railway needs to be addressed: it is here taken as a prepared way of rails to accommodate specially adapted rolling stock. The rails can be of any section (most sections, likely and unlikely, have been tried at one time or another) and the wheels can be flanged or plain. The invention of the wheel is shrouded in antiquity, but it does not take much imagination to devise a way of making a wheeled vehicle follow a pre-set path. The main application of a self-steering system was in conditions of total darkness where a man could not see to steer a truck. Such conditions existed underground, in mines.

The first railways of which there are definite records were the mining tramways of the sixteenth century, as described and illustrated by Agricola. It was quickly realised that a truck of coal running on flat wooden planks was much easier to push than one running on the rocky floor of a mine gallery. It was, however, soon found that if the truck were to be pushed along in total darkness, then some means was needed to hold it on course. The system devised consisted of arranging planks on the floor with a gap of about 6in between them, and fixing a vertical pin

Fig. 2. This hand-propelled truck has plain roller-type wheels, which are kept on the board 'rails' by the pin projecting down between them. In a mine this truck would keep to the track even when pushed along in total darkness. (Demonstration replica at the National Railway Museum, York) (*Author*)

Fig. 3. An example of wooden track preserved at the National Railway Museum, York. (*Author*)

on the front of the trucks to engage in this gap. The truck was called a *hund* by the German miners, and the pin was termed a *leitnagel*. This system is shown in Fig. 2.

Above ground, wooden rails were popular. The name 'rail' comes from rail-and-post fencing, which can still be seen in places. Wooden rails were cheap and easy to lay, repair and renew; they were soon very popular. They did, however, have one drawback: they wore out quickly. So the custom soon became widespread of laying a second, renewable, strip on the top of the 'permanent' rail. Where these strips were made of iron, they were known as 'plates' and the men who looked after them became known as 'platelayers' – a term still in use.

Wooden rails were often used in conjunction with wooden wheels; cast-iron wheels wore the rails out even faster. But wooden wheels tended to slip on the rails in wet weather, which made braking difficult. Slipping on wet rails is a problem also faced by modern railways.

There was once an extensive system of wooden railways in the North-East, all conveying coal from the mines to the rivers Tyne, Tees and Wear. Here the coal was loaded onto ships, either for export or for the coastal trade, principally to London. Traction on these railways was supplied by horses. All these routes were eventually relaid with iron rails, either as plateways or as edge railways, and many have been repeatedly upgraded to become main line railways.

The distance between the rails, or the track gauge, differed. In the North-East it varied between 4ft 6in and 5ft, while in Shropshire at Ironbridge in the Severn Gorge it was around 3ft. The two areas developed independently of each other, and the reasons for the two sizes are largely historical: a wooden 'chaldron'* wagon in the North-East made a full load for a single horse, while in Shropshire it was usual for a horse to pull two or three trucks. In the North-East, the general lie of the railways was downhill, from the pits to the staithes on the river banks where the coal was loaded into ships for export. Wagons were fitted with good brakes, but these were sometimes insufficient when wooden or cast-iron wheels slipped on wet wooden rails.

Some means had to be found of keeping wheels on the plain, rectangular rails (see Fig. 3). A flange was added to the wheel. Projecting below the level of the rail top, it stopped the wheel from slipping off in one direction, and a flange on the opposite side kept it from slipping off in the other. This pre-supposed, of course, that the wheels could not slide along their axles.

* The 'chaldron', incidentally, was a measure of weight. In 1616 it stood at about 43cwt, and it was fixed by statute in 1678 at 52½cwt. In 1695 it became 53cwt and remained so. By the second half of the eighteenth century the expression 'chaldron wagon' appeared, soon abbreviated to 'chaldron', which became synonymous with 'wagon'.

Fig. 4. The Nantlle Tramway on 23 September 1958, just after closure. The wagons' extended axles, allowing the wheels to adjust to variations in gauge, can just be seen. In the background is the cable-worked incline leading to the quarries. This was worked on the funicular principle: loaded slate wagons descending the incline pulled empty wagons up. (*R.M. Casserley*)

Generally flanges are on the inside of the wheels, but there have been one or two isolated lines where they were on the outside. Only slightly more common was the line with flanges on both sides of the wheels. This was to accommodate simply appalling track which kept to gauge plus or minus several inches! The Nantlle Railway in North Wales was one such. Here, the track gauge was nominally 3ft 6in, but the wheels could slide along their axles to take up variations in gauge. The Nantlle was horse-operated, and lasted long enough to be closed by British Railways in the 1950s.

So far, we have considered plain rails carrying flanged wheels. A rival system developed, whereby plain wheels ran on **L**-shaped rails. The perceived advantage was that wagons with plain wheels could also run on the public roads. This was not really true, because the wheels were necessarily of narrow tread – about 1in – and they soon bogged down in the unmetalled roads of the times. Turnpike road operators soon laid down a minimum tread width to avoid damage to their roads' surfaces. The narrow wheel rims are clearly shown in Fig. 6.

Pointwork presented no problem, apart from arranging that the rails did not trip up the horses

Fig. 5. Stone sleeper blocks on the Silkstone Tramway, South Yorkshire. The layout of the blocks shows the location of a passing place. (*Author*)

Fig. 6. Plateway track displayed at the National Railway Museum, York. It will be seen that the rails are quite short, with the joints supported in a cast-iron 'chair'. (*Author*)

Fig. 7. Plateways were almost always horse-operated, but here is an example of a steam locomotive on the plateway track at the Horsehay Works of the Coalbrookdale Company. The photograph is thought to have been taken *c.* 1880, but nothing more is known of this most interesting little locomotive. (*Courtesy Ironbridge Gorge Museum Trust*)

Many years ago now, your author and his wife found themselves in Merthyr Tydfil, and took the opportunity to visit the most famous plateway of them all, namely the Penydarren Tramway. It was here that Richard Trevithick demonstrated what has often been claimed to be the world's first steam railway locomotive in March 1804. We found the course of the line well preserved in places, with many stone sleeper blocks still *in situ*. And here was a historical conundrum: the sleepers suggested that the rails had been 4ft 8in or 4ft 9in apart. Yet the well-known drawing of the Penydarren locomotive has the wheels only 3ft apart. This led to further research, and your author is now convinced that the drawing, usually referred to as the Llewellyn Drawing and now in the Science Museum at South Kensington, does not show the 1804 Penydarren locomotive. He believes that it shows something even older, which almost certainly operated on the 3ft gauge internal tramways of the Penydarren Ironworks itself in 1802 or 1803.

pulling the wagons. The drawback to plateways was that the **L**-shaped rails, or plates, soon became clogged with dirt and rubbish. This did not fall off, but collected in the angle of the plates and resulted in wagons getting a very rough passage. It also reduced the hauling capacity of the horses that supplied the motive power. However, if a handful of dirt is dropped onto a modern rail, most of it will fall off. What remains will move when the rail vibrates at the approach of a train.

Curves were a potential problem. It is possible to bend a **I**-section rail to a continuous curve, but not so **L**-section ones. Curves were built up by a series of tangents, which meant that rails were limited to 3ft to 6ft lengths. The rough, jarring motion when traversing a curve was no problem when traffic moved at the speed of a horse led by a man, namely walking pace, but anything faster would have been unacceptable. This, and the inability of cast iron to support a heavy load, goes a long way to explain the general lack of success of steam locomotives on plateways. Indeed, several plateways that tried locomotives found that breakages were so frequent that they reverted to horse traction.

Plateways had a good innings. The last one, in the Forest of Dean, closed in 1944, but a demonstration plateway has been assembled at Blists Hill Open Air Museum, Coalbrookdale. This not only displays pointwork, but also includes some rolling stock – including that rarest of items, a plateway tank wagon.

EDGE RAILS OF IRON AND STEEL

C ast-iron rails were cheap to make. Usually in 6ft lengths, they were laid on separate stone sleeper blocks to leave a clear path down the centre of the track for the horses that provided traction. The Silkstone tramway in South Yorkshire was unusual in that its sleeper blocks were laid in a diamond form, rather than the usual rectangular layout. The cross-section of the rails could be almost anything – **T**-section, **T**-section, **I**-section, plain rectangular were all tried.

The Vale of Belvoir Railway track, illustrated in Fig. 8, shows an unusual form of interlocked joint between rails. This was ingenious, but it was soon found that odd gaps had to be filled with short stretches of rail. The interlocked system was simply not suitable for joining to plain-cut pieces of rail and so did not become commonplace.

Cast iron is strong in compression but brittle in tension. Between sleeper blocks, where it was unsupported, it was strong enough to support the horse-drawn wagons but not the pioneer steam locomotives,

Fig. 8. Cast-iron rails from the Vale of Belvoir Railway, which opened in 1815. Note that the rails are shaped so that they interlock with each other. (*Author*)

Fig. 9. An example of **T**-section rail at the National Railway Museum. Note the method of securing the rail to the 'chairs', and the rough-hewn sleepers. (*Author*)

Fig. 10. Malleable fish-bellied rail in longer lengths than between the stone sleepers. (*Author*)

which weighed 3 or 4 tons and had an axle-load of between 1 and 2 tons. The more expensive wrought iron was tried and found to be far less prone to breaking. In 1820 John Birkenshaw of the Bedlington Ironworks in Northumberland produced a **T**-section rail with a 'fish-bellied' cross-section in malleable iron. The fish-bellied section, first used in the cast-iron rails of William Jessop, was produced by a system of cams operating rolls. The first type produced was of 17lb/yard, but the Stockton & Darlington Railway, opened in 1825, used 28lb/yard, later increased to 35lb/yard. These rails were secured in the chairs with iron pins, rather after the fashion of Fig. 9. It is said that by 1837 parallel rails of 50lb/yard were in use, and 64lb/yard by 1842. These were used with iron chairs and secured by wedges. By 1841 Bolckow & Vaughan's Middlesbrough Iron Works was rolling rails of 73lb/yard for the Great North of England Railway. Stone sleeper blocks were used which were drilled with two holes, plugged with hammered in oak pins; the chairs were spiked to the oak. Wrought-iron rails with a square section had been used elsewhere for several years before Birkenshaw developed his fish-bellied section, but they were inferior to the Birkenshaw product.

Another attempt to combine a steam locomotive with brittle cast-iron rails involved putting the locomotive on more than four wheels. This was tried by William Hedley (1779–1843) at Wylam, and produced the world's first eight-wheeled locomotive – also the first articulated locomotive. It was mounted on two four-wheeled trucks or bogies and all wheels were driven by gearing. But it was ahead of its time: keeping the complicated machinery in order was quite an assignment, and the locomotive spent more time under repair than in service. It was converted back to a four-wheeler.

Stone sleeper blocks, while adequate for horse-drawn traffic, soon proved unsuitable for locomotives. They were used on the Stockton &

Darlington Railway, but as soon as horse traction for passenger services was abandoned, the line was relaid with wooden sleepers. The reason for this is not hard to deduce: the sideways thrusts of a locomotive's wheels tended to force the blocks out of gauge, and one rail tended to subside more than the other. So wooden sleepers were adopted, and the rails could be fastened down to something that could be relied upon to hold the gauge.

The next step was the adoption of a dumbbell-section rail, with the two heads identical. This 'double-headed' rail was mounted in cast-iron supports, termed 'chairs', and wedged in place with wooden wedges or 'keys'. When one head became worn, the whole rail could be turned upside-down and the other head used for traffic. It was an ingenious idea, but it failed because the chairs left definite imprints on the underside of the rail, thus making it useless for running. It was replaced by a rail, still dumbbell-shaped in section, but with the top half appreciably larger than the bottom, which was secured in chairs as before. This was termed a 'bull-head' rail, and it can still be seen in service today.

Steel-making had been practised since at least medieval times, always on a small scale and with variable, not to say unpredictable, results. It was only with the development of the Bessemer converter in 1856, which allowed steel-making on a large scale, that steel rails became possible. The first were introduced in 1857 on the Midland Railway and the London & North Western Railway. They lasted much longer, but were appreciably more expensive. The railway companies were cautious about the new material: the cost was high, and little value as scrap metal was perceived for worn rails. Advantage was then taken of the rolling mill process to produce longer rails. The London & North Western Railway led the way by rolling 60ft lengths at Crewe in the 1880s, a length that had become common by 1914. From 1979 120ft lengths were introduced. Each extension in length reduced the need for fished joints. This not only gave a smoother ride but also reduced the cost of joints and their maintenance.

Steel of controlled quality in abundant quantities was assured with the introduction of the Siemens-Martin open-hearth method in 1864, and the metal produced was put to many other uses besides rails. In fact, most steel manufacturers produced rails more or less as a side-line. With the nationalisation of the steel industry in 1967 the new British Steel Corporation concentrated rail production at Workington, home of the Workington Iron & Steel Company (latterly a subsidiary of the United Steel Co. Ltd), where rails had been produced since 1876. Today, steel 'blooms', or heavy rectangular bars, are produced at Teesside and taken to Workington by rail to be rolled into – rails! Typical steel compositions for rails are shown in Table 1.

Flat-bottomed rails are manufactured in 60, 70, 75, 80, 90, 95, 100, 110 and 113 lbs/yard, plus light rails, conductor rails, and special sections for switches and crossings. The specification for conductor rails is quite different and is shown in Table 2. Again, the balance, up to 100%, is iron. The conductor rail has low residuals to maximise electrical conductivity.

Table 1

Specification	Carbon%	Silicon%	Manganese%	Phosphorus%	Sulphur%
BS11 Normal	0.45–0.6	0.05–0.35	0.95–1.25	0.025 max	0.040 max
350 heat treated	0.70–0.82	0.13–0.60	0.65–1.25	0.025 max	0.008–0.03

The balance, up to 100%, is iron.

Table 2

Specification	Carbon%	Silicon%	Manganese%	Phosphorus%	Sulphur%
Conductor rail (typical)	0.08 max	0.05 max	0.30 max	0.05 max	0.05 max

Rails are manufactured by heating a steel bloom until it is bright red hot and has a degree of plasticity. It is then passed between the rolls of a rolling mill, which looks rather like a giant kitchen mangle. In much the same way that pastry becomes longer when it is rolled out thin in the kitchen, steel becomes longer when the blooms are rolled. Several passes are made, each time bringing the material closer to the desired size. The rolls have grooves cut into them, so that the steel, as it emerges, has the profile of a rail. The rolls are not quite symmetrical and as a result the emerging rail is 6 degrees off the horizontal. The purpose of this is to take account of the fact that the rolls wear, and to facilitate their reprofiling after the production of between 1,000 and 1,500 tons. Since the mid-1980s British Steel at Workington has developed an electric induction treatment which produces a rail with a hardened head. This has since been replaced by an on-line heat treatment process, utilising the heat that remains in the rail immediately after rolling. The head of the rail is cooled by water sprays from 850°C to 500°C, thereby producing a refined microstructure which resists wear in a similar manner to an electric induction hardened rail. Consequently the electrical induction process has now been discontinued. More expensive than the conventional product, most of this rail is exported and it finds only occasional use in Britain.

A further development in bloom manufacture at Teesside is continuous casting. Instead of ingots being produced, then reheated and rolled, the molten steel is poured (or teemed, as it is called), straight into a casting machine to produce blooms in a single operation. Costs are saved on a massive scale and there is less wastage. The continuously cast bloom is then cut into convenient lengths, ready for transport to Workington.

Wear is important, as steel fatigues with use. If the rate of wear exceeds that of fatigue, then cracks will wear away instead of growing in the rail. If very wear resistant rails are used in locations of low wear, then cracks may develop and if they remain undetected the rail will

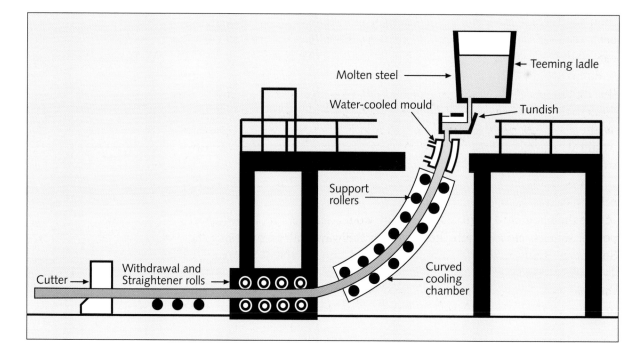

Molten steel

Teeming ladle

Water-cooled mould

Tundish

Support rollers

Curved cooling chamber

Cutter

Withdrawal and Straightener rolls

Fig. 11. The continuous casting process. (based on material supplied by *British Steel*)

eventually break. To avoid this the affected rail must be replaced. The alternative is to introduce 'artificial wear' by grinding the rail surface, a solution that finds favour in some countries. British Rail and Railtrack have largely defeated the problem by choosing a softer grade of steel than most European railways for most applications, resulting in higher wear and lower crack formation. But the problem has not been beaten absolutely. The occasional broken rail still occurs, but is so rare as to be regarded by the media as highly newsworthy.

The reason why rails break is worth discussing, especially in the light of the Hatfield accident on 17 October 2000. Defects can arise within the rail, either as a result of welding or a flaw in the manufacturing process. A minute pinhead of gas, trapped in the hot metal, results in a weakness invisible to the eye and only detectable by ultrasonic equipment. There is only one cure – replacement. This flaw, if unchecked, will develop until the rail snaps under a train, and this may have been the cause of the Hatfield accident. Defects arising outside the rail include weaknesses caused by faulty welds, drilling holes in a rail for signalling, track circuiting and other purposes, and wheelburns, where a braked wheel has skidded along the rail. Gauge corner cracking is a phenomenon which has only appeared within the last ten years and is not yet fully understood. It is thought to be caused by the stresses of wheel against rail at very high speeds, and results in a series of cracks, each running from the top centre of the rail to the inside of the head. Again, the only remedy is replacement. This book will be with the printers before the report into the Hatfield accident becomes available, and so further comment would be inappropriate at this time.

The action of wheels on the rail tops causes the phenomenon termed 'cold rolling'. That is to say, it causes the top of the rail to become longer than the bottom, producing a vertical curve in the rail. When rails have been removed for renewal and are lying by the trackside, this condition can often be clearly seen.

Rail is sold by the ton, so, provided the cost of the material is constant, the lighter the rail section specified, the more rail one gets for one's money. There was once a strong temptation, especially in countries such as the USA and Russia, to get the track laid with the lightest rail that would conceivably do the job, and upgrade the permanent way once sufficient revenue had been earned to meet the cost.

It was traditional, while supplying rail in 60ft lengths, to expect the railway company or customer to accept a percentage of 'shorts', or rails of less than standard length. The railway would use them to fill in gaps at points, sidings, etc., though the Southern Railway, and its successor the Southern Region, would sometimes weld them into 60ft lengths. Typically, the level of 'shorts' would be between 5 and 7.5 per cent, but this was open to negotiation: to this day London Underground Ltd tends to frown on shorts.

RAIL SIZES

Robert Hudson Ltd of Gildersome, Leeds, well-known as a supplier of light railway track for contractors' use, produced the diagrams that follow. They give some idea of the various rail sections then available in 1957. The weight of rails for main line use in the UK has now reached 113lb per yard. The modern BS113A rail section, 113lb/yd, replaced the previous BS110 section in about 1970. BS113A has a thicker web, intended to reduce metal fatigue at joints. As noted above, modern steelworks plant now makes it possible to produce rail in 120ft lengths, but modern welding techniques mean rails can be supplied in lengths of 600ft, which is standard for Railtrack. There is enough 'give' in the rails for several such lengths to be secured onto a train of flat wagons. They will flex with the train when it passes through points and curves.

Fig. 12. Sections of 60lb flat-bottomed rail. (*Robert Hudson Ltd*)

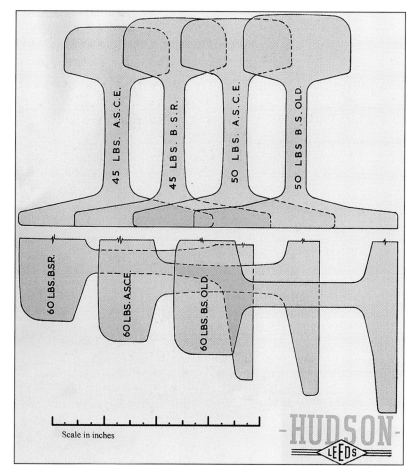

Occasionally it is necessary to join rails of different sizes, and even of different sections and weights. This calls for special fishplates, and an example is given in Fig. 13.

FLAT-BOTTOMED RAILS

In 1837 Charles B. Vignoles (1793–1875) devised the flat-bottomed rail shown in Fig. 14. The idea was to get rid of chairs and other fixings, and simply spike the rail down to the wooden sleepers. This made a rough-and-ready track where speed of construction was more important than anything else, and most of the railways in North America were originally laid in this fashion. But it was soon found that the foot of the rail cut into the sleepers, and some sort of baseplate was necessary. The rail became extremely popular and is now virtually standard throughout the world.

Laying track calls for the services of a surveyor to ensure that the rails actually go down where they are intended. The task of making sure that straight track really is straight is done by nothing more sophisticated than the human eye! Fig. 15 shows the method. The operative checks for vertical as well as horizontal alignment: humps and dips must be smoothed out by packing the ballast. The track in this instance is bull-head rail laid on concrete sleepers made by Dow-Mac.

Trying to ensure vertical alignment can have odd results. On the face of it, there is no reason why a thicker layer of ballast should not be spread and heavier (i.e. higher) rails employed when upgrading track. But

Fig. 13. A joint between flat-bottomed and bull-head rail, showing the special fishplate employed. Note also the bolt-and-clip fastening to the Dow-Mac concrete sleepers. The rust on the surface of the rails shows that this siding sees very little use. (*Author*)

Fig. 14. Flat bottom rail laid on wooden sleepers, with two different types of base plates and fastenings. (*Author*)

Fig. 15. Here a stretch of main line is being re-sleepered, with concrete sleepers, late 1930s. The ganger is sighting along the rail to check alignment. (*Author's collection*)

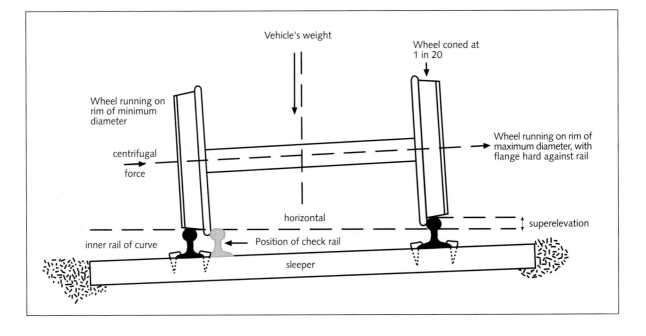

Fig. 16. Behaviour of flanged wheels on a curve.

the engineer needs to remember the loading gauge. If the level of the track is raised, say in a tunnel, there will be a risk of the trains coming into contact with the tunnel roof. Enlarging the tunnel will at best be an extremely expensive operation, causing the line to be closed intermittently, and may well simply not be an option. In the case of a tunnel, the foundation of the track must be excavated before fresh ballast is laid. So ballast thickness may vary, and there are instances of tracks appearing to 'dive' under overbridges!

Laying curved track is a rather different process. Sighting along the rails is still used, but the aim is to discern a line that is pleasing to the eye. The actual arc is quite complex. Readers who are familiar with toy train sets will recall joining straight track to curves of pre-set radius, and watching the train jerk violently as it leaves the straight bend. Precisely to avoid this scenario, the entrance to a curve is made much more gradual, so that the radius decreases from infinity (a straight line) to the desired figure. The result is a curve of constantly changing radius, which is known as a transition curve.

It is worth considering the behaviour of a rail vehicle in these conditions. The drawing at Fig. 16 gives the general idea. It will be noted that the wheels are coned, and centrifugal force pushes them outwards, so that the largest diameter of the outside wheel and the smallest diameter of the inside wheel are bearing on the rails. It will also be noted that the outside rail is raised by packing extra ballast under the outside end of the sleepers to counteract the centrifugal force. Centrifugal force can be discounted at low speeds, up to about 8mph, but at high speed it can derail a train. On really sharp curves, the cant or 'superelevation' can be several inches.

A note on the drawing in Fig. 16 refers to a check rail, and an example is shown in Fig. 17. We have seen that centrifugal force impels the wheel flanges against the outside rail. There is a risk that the flange might climb the rail and so effect a derailment. To counteract this, an extra rail,

Fig. 17. A4 class 4–6–2
No. 60007 *Sir Nigel Gresley*
arrives at Pickering, North Yorks
Moors Railway, 1999. Note the
continuous check rail on the
inside curve of the nearer track.
(*Author*)

termed a check rail, is laid so that the inside edge of the inner wheel flange bears against it, and so reduces the chances of a derailment. Check rails are mandatory on curves of 200 metres radius or less.

Now a word or two about the end of the track. Tracks end with buffer stops, ranging from the impressive hydraulic buffers to be seen at major termini down to – nothing at all! Fig. 18 illustrates a very common buffer stop built up from rail. Also common, but more in country areas, was a buffer stop consisting of a wooden palisade filled with earth. Occasionally a makeshift stop of a spare sleeper resting across the rail ends can be seen, and sometimes a pair of steel fittings designed to fit the curve of a wagon wheel appears. Finally, buffer stops may be completely absent and it is then up to the railwaymen not to shunt wagons over the edge. Of course, if the surrounding ground is built up to rail level, and the ground is firm, this may not matter too much, provided care is taken.

And how effective are buffer stops, anyway? The answer has to be somewhat ambivalent. While vehicles parked at buffer stops could generally be relied upon to behave themselves, buffers would not withstand being hit at speed by a train. The results could be amusing or tragic, and they were always unlooked for. On 2 February 1913 a train arrived at Crystal Palace station and the driver's attention was distracted. He failed to reduce his speed sufficiently, with the result that the locomotive demolished the buffers and went over the station forecourt for some 20ft, before crashing into the public lavatories. The solitary

Fig. 18. This rather amusing situation, a buffer stops and a gradient post, was photographed at Burnham on Sea, Somerset & Dorset Joint Railway. The gradient post was erected when the line continued down the quay beyond. It tells us that the gradient down to the buffer stops is 1 in 23, while in the opposite direction it is down at 1 in 51. As it stands, a wagon left at the buffer stops with its brakes off could be trusted (provided the local hooligans left it alone) not to roll away down the siding. (*Author*)

occupant made a heroic dash for safety, but was forced to abandon his jacket, overcoat and hat in the process. Three passengers and the fireman were slightly injured. Damage came to £316, including a payment of £17 to the gentleman caught with his trousers down.

The track gauge in Great Britain is 4ft 8½in, colloquially known as 'the four-foot'. 'The six-foot' is the distance between tracks on double or multiple tracks. It is 11ft 2in from track centre to centre. It is not unusual for pegs to be inserted into the ballast in 'the six-foot' and in the centre of a single line, to act as a datum point from which the individual tracks can be aligned. Centrifugal force will tend to push tracks outwards, especially on curves, and so occasionally they have to be pulled back into position. At one time an army of men with crowbars would lever the rails back, but modern track is so heavy (and labour so expensive) that resort is usually made to jacking.

We might end this chapter with a brief reference to a phenomenon sometimes referred to as 'roaring rails'. A sudden loud roaring noise from the track, it is roughly paralleled by the ground noise produced by certain

Your author recalls returning to Guildford station on 18 September 1953 after school to find the place in uproar. An electric train from Effingham Junction had arrived at Platform 1, a bay platform, and had overrun the buffers. The leading bogie of the first coach had been sheared off, but the coach body had gone over the buffers and crashed into the stationmaster's office. The cause of the accident was that the driver had mismanaged the combined electro-pneumatic and Westinghouse brake, and then in a flurry had actually applied forward power while attempting to put the train into reverse. Two passengers and five railway staff were injured, including the stationmaster and relief assistant stationmaster. Sadly, the relief assistant stationmaster later died of his injuries.

Fig. 19. A new siding has just been laid at Bolton Abbey Station, Yorkshire Dales Railway, and the permanent way engineers have inserted a datum peg just in front of the last of the crossing timbers. Painted white, it does not show up too well against the newly-laid ballast. (*Author*)

motorway surfaces, and, like its motorway counterpart, no one quite knows why it occurs. Although some research has been undertaken into this phenomenon, its cause is something of a mystery. One theory holds that it is due to vibration between the wheel and the rail, while another, with particular reference to the Southern Region of British Railways, attributes it to irregular wear of the rail because of variations in the work hardening of the surface from one point to another. The author wonders whether it might be due to local relaying using rails of slightly different steel composition – but this, it must be emphasised, is purely a guess based on not a shred of evidence!

In the author's experience, it occurred near Putney station, west London, where the sequence of points beneath a fast electric train produced a series of sounds quite reminiscent of Johann Strauss's 'Trisch-Trasch Polka'! It also occurred, over a quite considerable distance, between Rouen and Paris (St Lazare) when the author was a schoolboy and spent a couple of holidays with a French family in Paris. Incidentally, he learned more French in six weeks than in the previous six years at school.

THREE

SOME OTHER SYSTEMS AND ODDITIES

BLENKINSOP'S SYSTEM

It was not at first appreciated that a smooth wheel could grip a smooth rail with sufficient friction to haul a worthwhile load, even though that fact had been demonstrated by Trevithick's earliest locomotives. So John Blenkinsop (1783–1831) experimented with a rack-and-pinion system on the railway linking his Middleton Colliery with Leeds. He had projections cast on the side of the rail, which engaged a toothed wheel mounted on the side of the locomotive. The railway was inaugurated in 1811, and the locomotives built for him by Matthew Murray (1765–1826) worked successfully for over twenty years. One or two other lines adopted this system, but there were problems: since the teeth of the driving wheel

Fig. 20. Blenkinsop rail, showing the cast projections that constitute a rack, and a toothed wheel engaged with it. Note that the head of the rail is T-shaped, accommodating flanged wheels. Pointwork, with the toothed wheel lower than the surface of the running rail, would be very difficult. (*Author*)

projected lower than the top of the running rails, the locomotives could not pass over pointwork. Also, the display at the National Railway Museum (Fig. 20) shows an axle with toothed wheels at either end mounted on track with the rack on both rails. It will be realised that, in the absence of some sort of differential, the locomotive would have problems traversing a curve.

BRUNEL'S BROAD GAUGE

The Great Western Railway's engineer, Isambard Kingdom Brunel (1806–1859), chose the unique gauge of 7ft ¼in for his track when he became engineer to the Great Western Railway in 1833. He also devised his own track system, with a bridge section rail continuously supported on longitudinal sleepers held to gauge by cross transoms at intervals. The cross transoms extended the full width of double tracks, and were also fixed to piles driven into the ground. After a few months, embankments and other earthworks settled, leaving the track standing on almost a mini-trestle. So the piles had to go. The scheme is shown at Fig. 21.

But the bridge rail served the Great Western well, and it lingered in sidings well into the twentieth century. The author recalls seeing some in

Fig. 21. The method of constructing Brunel's baulk road. (*Drawing J.N. Slinn*)

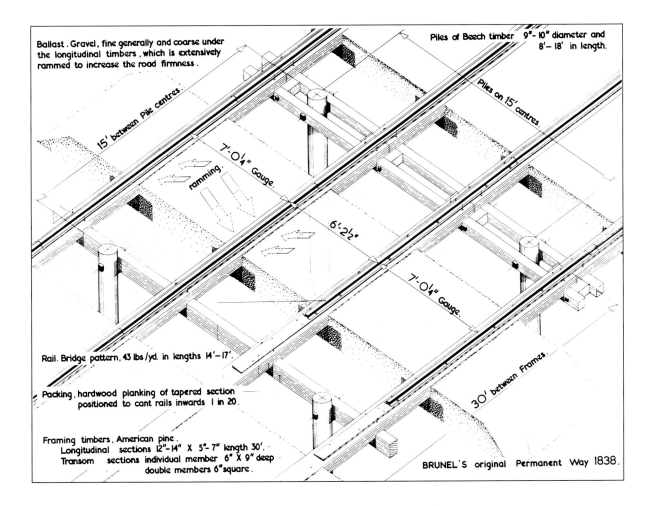

Ballast. Gravel, fine generally and coarse under the longitudinal timbers, which is extensively rammed to increase the road firmness.

Piles of Beech timber 9"- 10" diameter and 8'- 18' in length.

15' between Pile centres.

Piles on 15' centres

7'-0¼" Gauge.

ramming.

6'-2½"

7'-0¼" Gauge.

30' between Frames.

Rail. Bridge pattern, 43 lbs/yd. in lengths 14'- 17'.

Packing. hardwood planking of tapered section positioned to cant rails inwards 1 in 20.

Framing timbers, American pine.
Longitudinal sections 12"-14" X 5"- 7" length 30'.
Transom sections individual member 6" X 9" deep double members 6"square.

BRUNEL'S original Permanent Way 1838.

Fig. 22. Bridge rail connected to bull-head rail in the cattle dock at Yealmpton station, 1957. The broad gauge had been abolished sixty-five years previously! The chair holding the bull-head rail is of a somewhat unusual pattern. (*Author*)

Fig. 23. Reproduction mixed gauge pointwork at Didcot. In the foreground, a standard gauge track leaves the broad gauge, and in the background two mixed gauge tracks converge. (*Author*)

Fig. 24. Cross-section of bridge rail. (*Author's collection*)

use at Yealmpton in 1957 (Fig. 22). Since it was continuously supported, it could be of lighter cross-section, and hence cheaper, than the usual bull-head rails used by other lines, and this was Brunel's objective. Even so, no fewer than fourteen sections were used, from 45lb/yd in 1838 to 120lb/yd in 1891.* The 'baulk road' was rather rigid, and Great Western locomotives were very well sprung to compensate. Bridge rails lingered longer, and even today can be seen serving the main line for which they were produced – as fence posts, drilled to take the wires.

Brunel had noted that, while wrought-iron rails were stronger than cast-iron ones and could take a heavier load, they wore out in four years compared with ten or twelve years' life for their predecessors. This was a result of the metallurgy of the times: the rolling process formed scale in the surface of the iron, resulting in a tendency to split in service. Brunel devised the bridge rail to combine a thin section with maximum strength. For its weight it was extremely strong; Sir John Wolfe Barry, writing in 1876, stated that Brunel's 62lb/yd rail was the equal of 75–80lb/yd of bull-head rail laid on transverse sleepers.

BARLOW'S RAIL

In 1849 William Henry Barlow (1812–1902) devised a curious rail, rather like an inverted Y. The idea was that a broad base would grip in the ballast, and sleepers would be unnecessary. One or two lines tried it,

* See J.N. Slinn, *Great Western Way* (Historical Model Railway Society, 1985), p. 123.

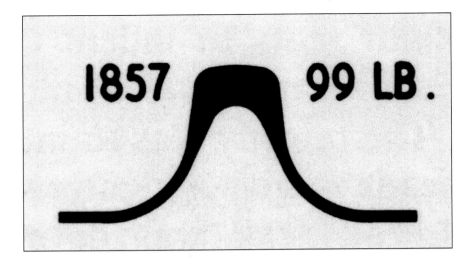

Fig. 25. Cross-section of Barlow's rail. (*Author's Collection*)

including the Great Western,* and the result was as one might expect: the rails spread beneath the trains and derailments were unacceptably frequent. However, Barlow's rail was used to construct Clevedon pier, where examples could still be seen in 1999 be seen.

STONE RAILWAYS

On Dartmoor, the local stone was used to produce the Haytor Tramway, a plateway with a difference. Opened in 1820, it operated until the late 1850s. Granite rails were hewn and, laid end to end, were heavy enough to make sleeper blocks unnecessary. Since they are quite useless for anything else, many of these rails are still to be seen *in situ*. The line seems to have operated successfully; no attempt was made during its thirty-year life to replace the granite with iron. Because the rails were laid on the ground without intermediate supports, a fracture would not matter, given the use of horse traction at walking pace. But such rails are extremely heavy to move, which would have made any replacement difficult.

RACK AND PINION RAILWAYS

Blenkinsop's rack-and-pinion system, which was designed to overcome the supposed lack of friction between a smooth rail and a smooth wheel, has already been discussed. It was soon realised that the 'cog-wheel' arrangement could be used to overcome very steep gradients. 1 in 100 is quite steep for a main line, 1 in 50 is severe, 1 in 36 calls for banking locomotives for all but the shortest trains, and 1 in 14 (on the Cromford & High Peak line) represented about the maximum that an orthodox locomotive could manage with two or three wagons in tow. But if the

* See Slinn, *Great Western Way*, p. 123.

Fig. 26. A close view of the Abt rack system at the Slovenian Railway Museum, Ljubljana. (*Author*)

Fig. 27. Abt rack-and-pinion pointwork at the summit of the Gornergrat Railway, above Zermatt, Switzerland. Notice how the section of straight rail alongside the rack is arranged to pivot with the rack to give a clear path for rail and rack through the crossing. Similar pointwork is used on the Snowdon Mountain Tramroad. (*Author*)

track were equipped with a central rail fitted with teeth, and a corresponding gear wheel were mounted under the locomotive, then gradients up to 1 in 10 were practicable. The only example in Britain is the Snowdon Mountain Tramroad, built with Swiss expertise and (until very recently) running Swiss locomotives. The earliest form of rack resembled a horizontal ladder, with two side pieces and rungs between them. It was invented in 1863 by a Swiss engineer named Nikolaus Riggenbach (1817–1899). The system used on Snowdon was patented in 1882 by another Swiss, Roman Abt (1850–1933), and consists of two rails laid side by side. Each rail has teeth milled into the top surface, and the two are laid in a staggered form, so that the teeth of one rail correspond to the gaps of the other. This means that the locomotive, which has two gear wheels underneath it, always has at least two teeth in mesh with the rack. The third system, to be found on the Mount Pilatus railway in Switzerland, has a central rail with teeth milled horizontally out of both sides. The pinions below the locomotives are horizontal, with vertical axles, and grip the central rack rail. This design was invented by yet another Swiss engineer, Eduard Locher-Freuler (1840–1910). As far as the author is aware, the Pilatus railway remains the system's sole application.

While the rack system enables trains to climb (and descend) quite steep inclines, it does have drawbacks. Speed with the rack in operation is limited to about 20mph. There is also the problem of a train joining the rack from plain track if the teeth of the pinion below the locomotive do not quite mesh with the rack itself. This is overcome, to some extent, by arranging the initial section of rack, about 20ft or so, to slide lengthways, with strong springs to bring it into position. Even so, as the author can testify from personal experience in Switzerland, when the train joins the rack it does so with a loud bang and quite a severe jolt. In the interests of braking, several axles below the train itself are also fitted with pinions. The Snowdon Mountain Tramroad gets over the problem by equipping all tracks with the rack, whether they are inclined or level. Below the Snowdon locomotives, it is only the pinion wheels that are powered; all wheels running on the ordinary rails are unpowered.

FELL RAILWAYS

Closely related to the rack-and-pinion systems is the centre-rail system devised by John Barraclough Fell (1815–1902). He developed in 1864–5 for a line over the Mont Cenis Pass. It can still be seen on the railway climbing Snaefell in the Isle of Man. Here a more or less ordinary bull-head rail is mounted horizontally between the running rails, and horizontal wheels are arranged below the railcars to grip the rail and thus secure extra adhesion. A similar system worked for many years in New Zealand to lift trains over the Rimutaka Incline; it was replaced by a tunnel through the mountain in 1955.

THE LARTIGUE MONORAIL

There have been several monorail systems proposed, including some with the carriages kept upright by means of gyroscopes, but the only one to move from the experimental to a practical application was the Lartigue system. Charles François Marie-Thérèse Lartigue (1834–1907) was a French engineer. His idea was for a single rail running along the top of a series of trestles, each shaped like an A. Level with the cross-brace was a guide rail on either side. The rail, which weighed 27lb/yard, was 3ft above the ground, and the guide rails were 2ft 4in below the running rail. The locomotives and rolling stock were arranged pannier-fashion astride the top rail which took practically all the weight. Lartigue claimed that earthworks would be minimal, and commended his system to the military

Fig. 28. Lartigue monorail locomotive, Listowel & Ballybunion Railway, Ireland, on 7 July 1914. The A-frame track is clearly shown. (*K.A.C.R. Nunn*)

– which showed virtually no interest. But there was a short line in France, employing vertical boiler locomotives, and a small demonstration line was erected in London, at Tothill Fields. This also employed a vertical boilered locomotive, built at Tubize, Belgium. But it was in Ireland, between Listowel and Ballybunion, that a really practical application for the system was built. Opening in 1888, it was 9¼ miles long, with one intermediate station. It is said to have cost £3,300 per mile. The passengers sat sideways, with their backs to the central rail; livestock travelled either side, balancing each other in pairs. A staircase over the rail, mounted on wheels, was marshalled in the train to enable passengers to cross from one side to the other. Points were impossible; trains moved from one track to another by curved turntables. Level crossings were replaced by drawbridges. The three locomotives shown in Figs 28, 29 and 30 were built by the Hunslet Engine Co. of Leeds. They had three powered axles, with a further two powered axles on the tenders. But this additional complication was seldom used. An old photograph shows that the Westminster vertical-boilered locomotive also found its way to the far west of Ireland, where it was used during the construction of the railway while the line's own locomotives were being built in Leeds.

The line was a disappointment to its shareholders. Estimates of traffic had been wildly over-optimistic, and during the winter months receipts were insufficient to pay working expenses. In 1897 a receiver was appointed, and the line struggled on until 1916. In that year it was taken over by the government, like all other Irish railways. The government relinquished control in 1921, and the line suffered damage during the Civil War of 1922. Lack of funds prevented repairs. Much to the annoyance and disappointment of its proprietors, the line was not included in the merger of railways within the Irish Free State to produce the Great Southern Railways, and closed on 14 October 1924 by order of the High Court of Dublin. At the time of closure it was said to be losing £30 a week.

Fig. 29. A train *en route*, showing how the line followed the contours of the ground with the minimum of earthworks. (*National Library of Dublin*)

Fig. 30. Liselton, the only intermediate station. The use of curved turntables instead of points is clearly shown, giving access to the passing loop. Note also the siding in the right foreground. (*National Library of Dublin*)

ATMOSPHERIC RAILWAYS

At the inception of the Liverpool & Manchester Railway, there was a strong body of opinion that it should be worked by cable traction. It was pointed out that the prime mover, a stationary engine, could be built as large and heavy as was necessary, whereas a locomotive had to be made small enough to pass through bridges and tunnels, and light enough not to damage rails or underline bridges. Moreover, unlike a locomotive, all the power of a stationary engine was available for traction since it did not have to move itself – apart, that is, from the power absorbed in moving the weight of the cable. Such cables were of hemp, prone to stretching, and needed frequent replacing.

The atmospheric railway was the same idea but in a new guise: instead of a cable, there would be a tube laid between the rails. A piston in the tube would be attached to the train, and a stationary engine would operate a pump to evacuate the air ahead of the piston. Atmospheric pressure behind the piston would propel it, and the train attached to it, along the track. Since the stationary engines did not have to move themselves, it was felt that gradients need no longer be a problem. There was the obvious difficulty that the piston would be inside the tube, and the train outside it: how were they to be connected? Various bright and not-so-bright ideas were put forward.

The railway track was quite normal, apart from the central tube. A detailed diagrammatic sketch revealing the working of the system is shown in Fig. 31. The slot along the top of the tube was for the arm connecting the piston with the train, and was sealed by a leather flap. Experiments gave very promising results, and when newly installed, its promise was great indeed. Several prominent engineers, including I.K. Brunel, were quite taken with the idea. Robert Stephenson, however, refused to have anything to do with the 'atmospheric caper', as he called it. Brunel, laying out the South Devon Railway, saved his employers a considerable sum of money by building the line with gradients as steep as 1 in 36. In practice, problems became apparent that had not shown up in experimental trials. On the South Devon Railway, the leather flap valve became hard and brittle when rain froze on it in winter and when it dried out in the heat of summer, with resulting loss of vacuum. So a lubricating grease was applied. As is well known, this grease became the staple diet of the local rats – they were quite partial to the leather flap as well – and loss of vacuum again ensued. The pumping stations were required to develop more power, and instances of trains coming to a standstill and having to be rescued by conventional locomotives followed. Brunel was forced to admit defeat, and the South Devon had to scrap all its expensive atmospheric installations – tubes, pumping engines, the entire system. Everything was disposed of by auction on 3 September 1855, with a loss to the shareholders of about £353,000. The South Devon was, however, left with a main line with gradients that were a severe headache to its operating department, and have remained a challenge for its successors ever since.

Another obvious problem for the continuous central tube was presented by pointwork. To try to solve this, the London & Croydon

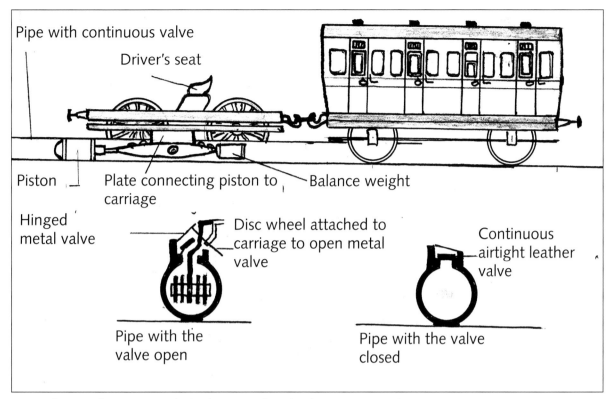

Pipe with continuous valve

Driver's seat

Piston

Plate connecting piston to carriage

Balance weight

Hinged metal valve

Disc wheel attached to carriage to open metal valve

Continuous airtight leather valve

Pipe with the valve open

Pipe with the valve closed

Fig. 31. The atmospheric system on the South Devon Railway. (*Author*)

Fig. 32. Atmospheric trains predated the age of photography, and contemporary drawings of them in motion are rare. This view of a piston carriage on the London & Croydon Railway shows the driver applying his hand brake. Behind him is a gauge showing the vacuum. The purpose of the lever is uncertain; it may have opened an emergency valve in the piston to bring the train to a standstill, but the usual method was to screw on the hand brakes and hold the train by the brake against the power of the vacuum. The ribbed pipe between the rails is clearly seen, and is very similar to that of the South Devon. (*Charles E. Lee*)

Railway installed at Norwood the world's first flyover junction, whereby the atmospheric trains passed over the lines to Brighton and Dover. Flyover junctions have been used in many locations where heavy traffic makes it advisable to avoid lines crossing on the level.

There were several other applications of the atmospheric principle, and all failed. The notion of a central power station powering trains along the line had to wait for the advent of electrification.

FUNICULAR RAILWAYS

The funicular is something of a rare bird in Britain, being limited to cliff railways and such like. Whilst the plain track is unremarkable, the pointwork employed in the Swiss example illustrated in Fig. 33 is most unusual in that it has no moving parts at all. The car's left-hand wheels have flanges on each side, while the right-hand wheels have no flanges at all. They do, however, have broad tyres, and, guided by the left-hand wheels, will roll across the rail surfaces in the direction of the cable in the centre of the track. The descending car has double-flanged wheels on the

Fig. 33. View from a car ascending to Chantarella above St Moritz, Switzerland, and about to enter the passing loop. (*Author*)

right, with broad-rimmed flangeless wheels on the left: it will keep to the right-hand track. The steepness of the line may be gauged from the steps on the left. The photograph also gives a glimpse of the guides and pulleys employed to keep the cable in its place. The steel sleepers are held in position by the continuous concrete foundation, with occasional gaps for drainage. The metal posts either side of the line support an overhead wire; this, however, is simply a telephone line between the driver and the winding station at the top. The Great Orme Railway in North Wales operates on a similar system, but avoids pointwork altogether by halting both cars at the intermediate station, where the winding engine is situated, and requiring passengers to change cars!

Finally, perhaps we might mention another variant sometimes termed 'cable railway'. This is an overhead system where a cable replaces the rails altogether. Slung from steel towers, such systems are rare in Britain but common overseas, especially in Switzerland as tourist attractions conveying visitors to mountain peaks and other viewpoints. The chair lift at a ski resort uses just one cable, which carries the cars and also provides the tractive power. A more sophisticated cable system uses a main carrying cable, a brake cable, and a haulage cable. With unsupported spans of up to a mile, such cables exert a tremendous strain on their supports simply by virtue of their own weight, and the cars are of the lightest construction commensurate with safety.

The freight variety, sometimes termed 'telpher', from the French *télépherique*, is used to convey minerals such as gravel and colliery waste in tipping cars that built up the slag heaps which were once such a common feature of the British industrial scene. But since the 'track' for these systems is a cable, and not rails, it might be argued that such installations are not really railways at all!

FOUR

POINTS AND CROSSINGS

Τhe problem of what happens when one track needs to divide into two has been solved in a variety of ways. Turntables were the first on the scene: the wagon was pushed onto the turntable, turned until it faced the desired track, and then pushed off. The process was then repeated for the next wagon, and so on. It will soon become apparent that for a train of any length this is a time-consuming and cumbersome method, but it does have its advantages where space is limited, and wagon turntables can still be found.

Turnouts (or points as they are often termed) were devised for plateways, and a simple example is shown in Fig. 36. If the moving parts were omitted altogether, it was necessary for the horse to give a good pull in the required direction. If one pair of wheels went one way, and the other pair went the other way, the person in charge had quite a bit of clearing up to do. There could be no problem if the turnout were approached from the trailing direction, however.

Fig. 34. A wagon turntable preserved at the National Railway Museum, York. Note the extremely short length, suitable for one four-wheeled wagon. (*Author*)

Fig. 35. This wagon turntable, also photographed at the National Railway Museum, was arranged to take three tracks, so that movement before a wagon could be shunted on was minimised. It was built from iron castings, as can be seen here, and would have been let into the ground so that the rail tops matched the level of the adjoining tracks. (*Author*)

Fig. 36. The parts for a simple turnout for a plateway, assembled as they would appear in use. The **L**-section rails would be mounted on stone sleeper blocks. Note the 'check' rail opposite the crossing, to guide the wheel onto the correct track. Some of the rails are cast to a curve. (*National Railway Museum*)

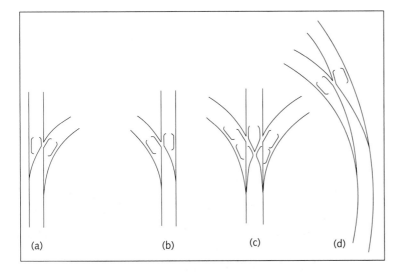

The various types of simple turnout are shown in Fig. 37. At (a) the main line goes straight ahead and the branch diverges to the right, so it is termed a right-hand turnout. At (b) the branch diverges to the left, so we have a left-hand turnout. (c) consists of (a) and (b) superimposed on each other, while (d) is either (a) or (b) with both tracks on a curve. All these layouts have their uses, with (a) and (b) in much the majority. (c) and (d) are more expensive to build, and therefore are only used when space considerations make them essential.

Fig. 37. Types of turnout. (a) Right-hand turnout (b) Left-hand turnout (c) Three-way point (d) Point on curve.

Junctions in double track were usually like these in Fig. 40(a). These involved two turnouts and a crossing, and, clearly, one track has to cross another. Consequently, a train running from A to B would conflict with a train running from C to A, and the signalling must be interlocked so that one train is halted while the other clears the junction. The type of junction shown at Fig. 40(b) is termed a single-lead junction. Although no fewer than four turnouts are required, the first cost of a crossing and the expense of maintaining it afterwards are avoided, and this is felt to be an advantage. The drawback is that, between points x and y, trains running from A to C are effectively on a single line, while between x and the crossover a train from C to A is also running 'wrong-line'. Thus a train from A to C cannot pass a train in the opposite direction, a manoeuvre which is perfectly safe with the

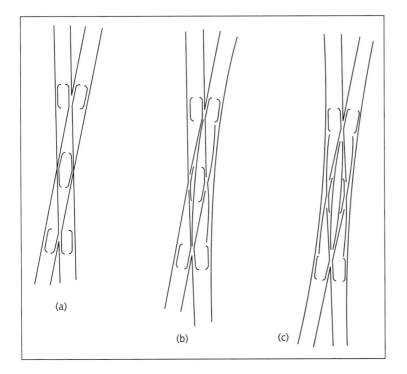

Fig. 38. Types of crossing. (a) Diamond crossing (b) Single slip (c) Double slip.

arrangement at Fig. 40(a). Nevertheless, with modern signalling, and especially where traffic on the branch is light, this was considered to be acceptable. But there have been a number of accidents, or near misses, at single-lead junctions. Although these junctions remain in use, there is something of a question mark over their further application.

There is a way of arranging for two tracks to merge into a single line, and then separate again, without any moving parts at all. Gauntletted or interlaced track was used from time to time, but was more common in America than in the UK. There were once one or two examples on the

Fig. 39. A double track junction. This is Staines in January 1927, before electrification. The train, headed by A12 class 0–4–2 No. E618, is taking the left-hand track towards Virginia Water and Reading. The right-hand track leads to Windsor. Note also that the junction of the two up lines is combined with a turnout to the sidings, making a three-way point. (*H.C. Casserley*)

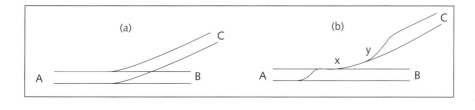

Fig. 40. Types of double junctions.

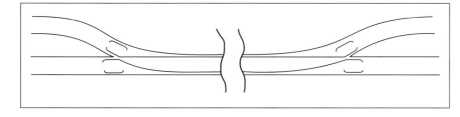

Fig. 41. The principle of gauntletted or interlaced track.

Highland Railway. Typical situations for the application of the system were the need to get a double track past either a narrow tunnel or a narrow bridge or viaduct, where widening to accommodate a second track was not practicable. The advantage was that there were no points to change, and hence no risk of a train taking up the wrong line when leaving the section. The drawback was the first cost of four rails instead of two, and the trackbed needed to be slightly wider than a true single line. The best known example is the Great Northern Railway of Ireland's bridge over the

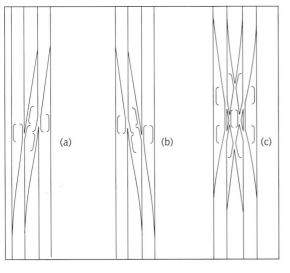

Fig. 42. Types of crossovers.
(a) Facing crossover (b) Trailing crossover (c) Scissors crossover.

Fig. 43. The diamond crossing at Newark. Here the Midland Railway's cross-country line (originally double track, now reduced to single) from Nottingham to Lincoln crosses the East Coast Main Line of the Great Northern Railway. (*Author*)

River Boyne at Dundalk. This high steel structure was built to take a single line, and widening it would have been prohibitively expensive, so gauntletted track was laid instead. It is, of course, signalled as a single line, although four rails are actually used. The idea also found application in street tramways (see Chapter 13).

The various types of diamond crossing are shown at Fig. 38. (a) is a simple crossing, where one track crosses another but it is not necessary to move from one to the other. It will be appreciated that there are no moving parts. Where the angle of crossing is small, a type of crossing with moving tongues is employed. This results in continuous support for the wheel and eliminates the gap in the centre of the crossing. At (b) we have a single slip: it is possible to move from one track, and only one track, to another. And at (c) we have a double slip: here it is possible to move from either track to the other, irrespective of the direction from which the slip is approached. Again, the simplest, (a), is by far the most common.

At Fig. 42 three types of crossover points are illustrated. Given that on double track in the UK trains run on the left, it will be seen that at (a) a train approaching on the left-hand track can run through onto the parallel track without reversing, because the points face the direction of travel, this is termed a facing crossover. At (b) a train must run through

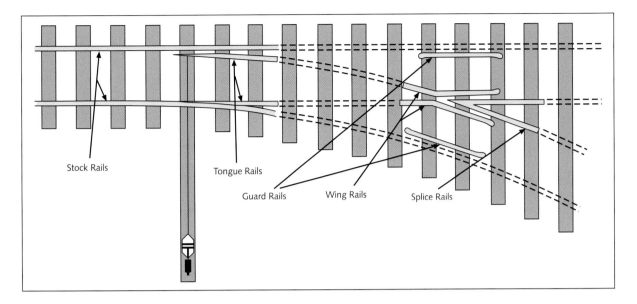

Stock Rails

Tongue Rails

Guard Rails   Wing Rails   Splice Rails

the crossover and then reverse to gain the opposite track; it is termed a trailing crossover. At (c) the two are superimposed; this is called a scissors crossover because of the supposed resemblance of the tracks to a pair of scissors. If the reader is puzzled by this, the author confesses that he can see a slight resemblance, but only a slight one!

Fig. 44 shows a simple turnout, whereby one track splits into two, or two tracks combine into a single line. The ends of the tongue rails are jointed by fishplates, which give them play to move under the control of the lever shown at the bottom left of the diagram; one tongue rail is pressed against the stock rail and the other is sufficiently far away from its adjacent stock rail to permit the passage of the wheel flanges. The guard rails press against the backs of the wheel flanges, and prevent the opposite wheel inadvertently taking the wrong side of the crossing.

The lever to operate the turnout can either be actually at the turnout, as shown here, for manual use by railway staff, or it can be operated from a distant signalbox, either mechanically by means of rodding attached to a lever in the 'box, or electrically, by means of a point motor, controlled by a switch in the signalbox. Over a distance of 350 yards* the rodding is too heavy to be moved manually, so either a second signalbox must be provided (and manned) to operate the points in question, or the much cheaper alternative of a point motor must be provided. The electricity supply is often provided by the signalman, with a hand-cranked generator! If passenger trains are to pass over the turnout, then the point control must be locked while the train passes. The subject of point and signal interlocking is really more appropriate to a book on signalling, of which there are several excellent examples available, and the interested reader is referred to them.†

Fig. 44. A simple turnout, showing the names of the constituent parts.

* In the 1870s, the maximum distance between a point and the signalbox that controlled it was 120 yards. This was progressively extended, until by 1925 it was 350 yards, the figure at which it remains. Thus it was common to find two signalboxes even at quite small stations.
† A selection is given in the Acknowledgements and Suggestions for Further Reading at the end of the book.

Figs 45–48 are illustrations of a turnout built up from bull-head rail. The tapering of the tongue rails will be clearly seen; this enables them to lie flat against the stock rails. Also, the crossing is visible, with its associated wing rails and guard or check rails.

It will be appreciated that if one line from the points is straight, the other must be on a curve. The radius of this curve dictates the speed at which the turnout can be taken, and this in turn depends on the length of the rail available to make the switch. In the 1840s, 10ft was about the limit. By 1939, the Great Western Railway was using 32ft switches, with a tapered tongue 17ft 3in long. When used with a 1 in 20 crossing, the

Fig. 45. This is the points end of a hand-operated turnout, showing the points set for the right-hand track (above) and the left-hand track (below). (*Author*)

permissible speed was about 50mph. At the time of writing, the latest switches are up to 91ft long with a 57ft 5in taper, and can be safely taken at 125mph.

For edge rails, two forms of turnout gained favour. First, the moving point type: this is illustrated in Figs. 45–48. Here, as long as the points remain unchanged under a moving vehicle, there is no risk of calamity. If the turnout is approached from the trailing direction and is incorrectly set, then the vehicle's wheels will move the points over, the vehicle will not be derailed, and the points will reset. But if the points are locked, the mechanism will be smashed and extensive (and expensive) repairs will be needed. Just occasionally, points are spring-operated, so that a passing loop can be traversed in either direction without the need to manipulate the points at all.

The actual crossing, although built up from rail, is handled as a single unit. An example is illustrated at Fig. 46. It will be seen that the rails are at an angle to each other, and hence a special chair is needed to hold them in place. One can be seen in Fig. 46, and is shown in close-up in Fig. 47.

The second type of turnout was the stub point. This avoided the difficult task of grinding or planing a pair of rails down to a point, and so was cheaper to manufacture. But if the turnout was approached from the trailing direction and was incorrectly set, then the vehicle would be derailed. At best, this resulted in damage and inconvenience; at worst, it could cause a

Fig. 46. A built-up crossing. (*Author*)

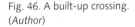

Fig. 47. An example of a special chair to secure rails at the correct angle for a crossing. (*Author*)

Fig. 48. A crossing (sometimes termed a 'frog') built up from bull-head rail. The rails are held in the chairs with wooden keys. Note the wing rails, and the check rails opposite. They ensure that the wheel flanges take the correct path through the crossing. This is from the same turnout as the points illustrated in Figs. 27–28. (*Author*)

Fig. 49. Stub points at the entrance to the Engine House, Camden Town, *c*. 1838. The operator on the right moves the two rails on which the locomotive is standing to align them with either the left- or right-hand track. (*Author's collection*)

serious accident. Stub points were common in the early days of railways (see Fig. 49), but have now disappeared (there was a rather famous three-way stub point at Portmadoc, Festiniog Railway (or Ffestiniog Railway, as it is spelt these days) but it was removed in the 1970s). They fell into disfavour on safety grounds, and the Board of Trade always took a jaundiced view of them.

Where one rail crosses another, provision has to be made for the wheel flanges to pass through. A typical crossing is illustrated at Fig. 48. It will be seen that there are short rails alongside the rails that actually carry the wheels; these are termed 'wing rails'. Their purpose is to guide the wheels by acting on the backs of the flanges to ensure that they follow the correct path. Similarly, the short rails mounted opposite, termed

Fig. 50. A cast manganese steel crossing at York. (*Author*)

'check rails', perform a similar function for wheels running in the opposite direction.

The crossing illustrated in Fig. 48 is built up from rail. This is a relatively inexpensive method of construction, and thousands of examples can be seen on today's railways. But for those few locations where traffic, and therefore wear and tear, are heaviest, the cast steel crossing has been developed. Cast in one piece, the steel contains 12 to 14 per cent manganese. Although between five and six times the price of ordinary carbon, such crossings made of manganese steel last proportionately longer and hence the intervals when the track has to be closed for renewal are fewer. Manufacture of these crossings was pioneered by two Sheffield steel firms, Edgar Allen Engineering Ltd and Hadfields Ltd. The manufacturing process guarantees accuracy. A famous example could once be seen just outside Newcastle station (Fig. 51), while the high-speed crossings at Worting Junction, near Basingstoke, in steam days could safely be taken at speeds of up to 60mph. Both these examples are on busy main lines. An example is shown in Fig. 50.

As well as having simple turnouts, tracks need to cross each other, and a simple diamond crossing is illustrated at Fig. 38. It takes its name, obviously enough, from the shape of the rails in the centre. Sometimes traffic is required to move from one track onto another, crossing at an angle: this is called either a single slip or a double slip. These are

Fig. 51. The diamond crossings at the south end of Newcastle Central station, *c.* 1970. Note that some of the tracks on the right are electrified with a third rail. In recent years, this layout has been considerably simplified. (*Rail Archive Stephenson*)

Fig. 52. A single slip at Embsay, Yorkshire Dales Railway, October 2000. Notice the point rodding. (*Author*)

illustrated in Figs 52 and 53. They are difficult to manufacture and very expensive. Two ordinary turnouts placed nose to nose will perform an identical function at a much lower initial cost. But two turnouts take up twice as much space, and where space is limited the single or double slip can be employed.

Let us now turn to catch points and trap points. They look very similar, and both have the purpose of derailing any vehicles whose continued movement is undesirable. Trap points are usually installed at exits from sidings, and are interlocked with the signals. If a train moves towards the main line and against the signal, it will be derailed before it can conflict with the main line, where another train might be passing. An example is

Fig. 53. A double slip at Ingrow West, Keighley & Worth Valley Railway, June 1998. (*Author*)

Fig.54. Trap points at Ribblehead, 1998. Any vehicle in the siding behind the camera will be derailed to the left if it moves towards the main line. The point is controlled from the ground frame in the centre background by the point rodding, which is clearly visible. Notice also that the two stock rails are clearly 'joggled' to enable the point rails to bed against them smoothly. (*Author*)

illustrated at Fig. 54. Catch points are placed on the main line, on a gradient and on double track. the catch point is often spring operated, and normally 'open' – that is to say, set to derail any vehicle passing through in the wrong direction. The normal direction of traffic is uphill, and the wheel flanges push the point blades over as they pass through. But should any vehicles become detached and run backwards, they would be derailed or diverted into a sand drag before they could cause further mischief. Sometimes catch points are lever operated, so that a train brought to a stand on them can be restarted, which often involves setting back, without difficulty. A prominent sign warns train crews to be careful, see Fig. 55.

Fig. 55. This scene is at Winsor Hill Tunnel on the Somerset & Dorset Joint Railway, and shows the down 'Pines Express' on double track. The photograph was taken on 31 March 1956. The train is running downhill. The catch points on the up line are spring operated: trains can pass through them without difficulty in the up direction, but any vehicle breaking away and running backwards will be derailed. A hand lever is provided so that a train stopped on the points will not be derailed if it is necessary for the locomotive to set back a few feet on restarting. Note also the prominent notice. (*Ivo Peters*)

Your author recalls an episode in the 1950s at North Camp, Southern Region. There was a refuge loop on one side of the up platform, making it an island. Where the refuge loop rejoined the main running line, there was, of course, a trap point. On the other side of the loop stood the cattle dock. On this occasion, whether by bad luck or bad judgement, the local goods train locomotive, an N class 2–6–0, finished up 'on the floor'. The close proximity of the station platform on one side and the cattle dock on the other meant that rerailing the engine with jacks and packing was out of the question, and it was eventually recovered by the Guildford breakdown crane at one end and the Reading crane at the other. The work was done at night after the last passenger train had gone, but the dislocation to the night freight traffic was quite considerable. No doubt someone had quite a bit of explaining to do.

The usual method of point operation, on the steam railway of yesteryear at any rate, was for the points to be moved by the signalman, who pulled a lever in the signalbox. The lever was linked to the point by an inverted-**U** or circular section rod, which enabled either a pull or a push to be transmitted, depending on how the points were to be set. But it was found that there was a limit to the distance over which even the strongest signalman could move a set of points. In these situations,

Fig. 56. A very simple ground frame arrangement at Ribblehead, 1998. The point rodding can be clearly seen. (*Author*)

Fig. 57. A typical point motor installation, 1999. The machine is housed in the casing to the left. (*Author*)

points were, and still are, moved by a point motor. This operates on the principle of a solenoid, and the rod connection is replaced by three electric cables. There are several types available from a number of manufacturers, and choice is often down to the personal preference of the engineer concerned.

Not all points are operated from a signalbox; Fig. 56 shows a ground frame, whereby several point levers are grouped together to form what is almost a mini-signalbox to enable one man to control the points in a station goods yard. Sometimes, however, a single point may have its own lever alongside, and Fig. 58 shows such a lever prior to installation. The lady holding it upright gives a good idea of its size.

Fig. 59. A simple reversing linkage for point rodding, photographed at Ribblehead. (*Author*)

Fig. 58. A point lever prior to installation. It has been lying in the open for a considerable period and is somewhat rusty, but it is so robustly constructed that a dose of oil is all that is needed to make it as good as new. (*Author*)

It is sometimes necessary to reverse the thrust of point rodding, and a simple linkage, shown at Fig. 59, is installed to effect this. It is of course necessary to ensure that the point does not move while a train is actually passing over it. To this end, the bar linking the point blades has two notches cut in it. When the point is fully home for either direction, one of these notches is in alignment with a movable bolt. This bolt is controlled from the signalbox by a locking lever, and the controlling signal cannot be cleared until the locking lever has been pulled. With the bolt in position, the point blades cannot move. But in practice, only those points

Fig. 60. A passing loop. Here the detector mechanism is set on the right-hand side of the track. The treadle against the right-hand rail adds further security: when the treadle is depressed by a wheel flange, the bolt between the rails is secured. (*Author*)

over which passenger trains will be worked are interlocked in this fashion. For freight traffic, shunting, etc., a simple lever suffices. But occasionally a passenger train needs to be worked over such points: a trailing crossover, not normally interlocked, may, for example, be used if temporary single-line working is in force while engineering works are carried out nearby. Then unlocked points must be secured, and this is done by 'clipping' them. The so-called clip is rather like a joiner's clamp, and it secures the point blade to the stock rail. It is usual to fit the clips with a lock or other device to ensure that they are not tampered with by unauthorised persons.

Fig. 61. A set of points secured with a clip to ensure safe passenger working. The clip can be seen between the two sleepers to the right: the threaded screw part is bolted tight to the stock rail while the other end encircles the foot of the rail and secures the point blade. A padlock can just be seen at the right-hand end. (*Author*)

FIVE

SLEEPERS AND FASTENINGS

The earliest sleepers were made of stone blocks and lasted for many years. They were used on the Stockton & Darlington Railway, on the Liverpool & Manchester Railway, and even on the London & Birmingham Railway. The stone sleeper was a solid block, supporting the rail fastening or chair. Gauge was maintained by the ballast alone, and the occasional tie bar. This was reasonably satisfactory for trains moving at about 20mph or so, but heavier locomotives running at faster speeds caused the track to become dislocated, resulting in the derailment of following trains. One early railway is even said to have tried to avoid the use of sleepers when making a cutting through solid rock: the rails were spiked down to the rock itself. The resulting ride was so hard that ballast and sleepers were soon substituted.

Timber sleepers were of elm or fir, both of which were cheap and readily available, and at first were untreated. The standard size is 9ft long, 10in wide, and 5in deep. Average weight was 237lbs. It was soon found that creosote could prolong the life of sleepers, and eventually the railways established works for the purpose. The timbers were placed in a drum, and the creosote was forced in under pressure. The result was that the timber was impregnated with the preservative. In later years, Australian jarrah and other hard woods, which do not need creosoting, replaced home-grown timber.

The traditional timber sleeper has been challenged by other materials. In tropical countries, it was found that wood was soon devoured by termites, and sleepers made of pressed steel were employed. Although the steel manufacturers (understandably) tried to promote steel sleepers in this country, and the Great Western experimented with them in the 1930s, their reception was at best luke-warm, and because of steel shortages, they were simply not available during the Second World War. Rust was perceived to be a problem, and steel sleepers need to be renewed more frequently than those made of other materials. Also, their spade-shaped ends made steel sleepers liable to move sideways on curves under the lateral forces of a moving train. But the use of computer-assisted design has produced a range of steel sleepers suitable for main line use, and a stretch of track was relaid with them in the 1990s on the West Coast Main Line, near Quintinshill in Scotland. But for secondary routes and sidings, steel sleepers have much to commend them. For instance,

36,400 steel sleepers were installed over 15 miles of the Settle and Carlisle line in 1999. Their pressed steel shape means that they can be stacked for storage, taking up less space, and hence they are easier to install. With shoulders for the Pandrol E-clip welded into position, a Type 400 sleeper weighs 80kg and can easily be lifted by two men. By contrast, it takes eight men using tongs to lift a concrete sleeper.

A perceived failing of steel sleepers used to be their lack of insulation – and hence their unsuitability for track circuits except in conjunction with insulating materials which might break down owing to wear and tear, wind and weather. But modern insulation seems to have overcome this, and where it has been installed no problems have been reported.

Much more successful is the reinforced concrete sleeper, which uses far less steel and is much cheaper. It is also much heavier, at 550lb complete with its two chairs and bolts. It has the advantage that the track is much more solid and less likely to distort under the weight of trains, but individual sleepers are more difficult to manhandle. The concrete sleeper, or something like it, is of respectable vintage: as early as 1919 the Weston, Clevedon & Portishead Railway was replacing defective wooden sleepers with home-made concrete blocks.

The wooden sleeper is a hardy creature with a lifespan of fifteen to eighteen years, although in some locations, such as tunnels or water troughs, it can fail a good deal sooner.

Fig. 62. An example of a pressed steel sleeper is shown (left), and a traditional timber sleeper (right). Both have flat-bottomed rail secured by spring steel clips. (*Author*)

The case of the disappearing sleepers! The Talyllyn Railway was laid in 1865 and received virtually no maintenance until the Preservation Society took over in 1950. By then, the track looked like a grassy path between two very overgrown hedges. The author recalls that, in about 1955, some enterprising volunteer rigged up a weed-killing wagon. It consisted of a slate wagon underframe supporting two oil drums, with piping down to the track welded from scaffolding pole. It was all too effective! We found that the sleepers had virtually rotted away, with the rails held to gauge by the weeds alone. So when we killed the weeds, the track dropped to pieces! The weedkilling wagon was accordingly sidelined until the track was strong enough to dispense with the weeds.

The success of concrete has had the curious effect of reintroducing the stone – or a kind of stone – sleeper. The author recalls seeing sidings on the Longmoor Military Railway laid on sleepers made from rectangular concrete blocks, with a steel tie-bar to maintain gauge. The Great Western Railway produced something similar just before the Second World War, which had the advantage of weighing only 246lb, little more than a conventional wooden sleeper. Now there are several different types of concrete sleeper, depending on the type of rail fastening required. These are cast integral with the concrete, and can be obtained either to gauge for straight track, or slightly wide of gauge for easy passage round curves. The range available is large: Tarmac Precast Concrete Ltd lists fifty-eight sleepers in its catalogue, with a further six types of crossing bearers. These are products of Tarmac's constituent companies, Costain Concrete and DowMac Concrete, and its own developments. A small sample is given in Table 3.

Fig. 63. Track laid with concrete blocks for sleepers and steel tie bars. Here the occasional timber sleeper can be seen. (*Author*)

Table 3

Type	Length*	Width at base*	Width at top*	Thickness at Ends*	Thickness at Centre*	Weight (kg)	Fastening System	Remarks
5F40	2420	285	200	210	175	295	Pandrol JG8	Unlimited use
F41	2420	285	200	210	175	295	Pandrol Fastclip	Unlimited use
F27A	2515	264	216	211	165	290	Pandrol JG5	Unlimited use
5EF28/ 5EF28(0)	2580	290	250	165	140	270	Pandrol JG5	Shallow depth sleeper for use in track where clearances or ground conditions require. Provision for standard conductor rail at one end.
EF32S	2580	290	250	174	140	280	Pandrol JG5	Shallow depth sleeper for use in track where clearances or ground conditions require. Provision for standard conductor rail at one end.
EF36/ EF36(0)	2420	290	250	165	140	270	Pandrol Fastclip	Shallow depth sleeper for use in track where clearances or ground conditions require. Provision for standard conductor rail at one end.
F40GW	2420	285	200	200	175	295	Pandrol JG8	For use where gauge widening required; with bolted check rail as necessary.
F43	2420	285	200	210	175	295	Vossloh W14	Unlimited use.
NTF504	2580	290	250	174	140	270	Pandrol 3906	Standard London Underground sleeper for surface and sub-surface ballasted track.
T600	650	290		275	–	211	As required	Twin block sleeper for both main line and light railway applications.
T601	2500	225	185	170	140	183	As required	For light railway applications.

* Dimensions in millimetres.

The concrete sleeper has come a long way in a comparatively short time. Now standard on the Railtrack network, its heavy weight, previously a handicap as compared with the timber sleeper, is now seen as an advantage for holding down long welded rails. There is, however, the possibility that cast-in rail fastenings may come into contact with the steel reinforcing bars, and thus render a track circuit ineffective.

Underground railways and rapid transit systems are increasingly turning to track laid in a concrete bed. Here the sleepers have projecting reinforcement bars, and the concrete is laid around them, or else the rail fixings are suspended in position and cast *in situ*. In either case conventional ballast is superseded. But, as is ever the case, absorbent pads are placed between the rails and their fixings to introduce the degree of resilience that is natural in wooden sleepers and conventional ballast and without which the ride would be very hard indeed, to say nothing of the incidence of broken springs.

Double-headed and bull-head rails, by virtue of their rounded undersides, need a special support or 'chair' to secure them to sleepers. The basic chair design was standardised at an early date, and Fig. 64 may be taken as typical of the bull-head era. Many thousands can still be seen in service today on branch lines and sidings. The number of fixing holes varied: the lightest and/or earliest had only two holes, while later, heavier specimens, which were expected to cope with heavier traffic, had three or four holes. Some railways adopted an S-shaped base for their chairs. The Ffestiniog Railway was one, and its design is illustrated in Fig. 65. The Manchester & Milford Railway used a similar-shaped chair. This design had the advantage that the chair spikes would not be in line with the grain of the sleeper, and so would be less likely to split it. With the advent of screws to secure chairs to sleepers, this advantage became less important.

Fig. 64. An example of a spring steel key and a wooden key side by side on the freight-only branch from Northallerton to Bedale, photographed in February 2000. The left-hand chair, with the steel key, needs replacing. This line, seeing only the occasional freight train, receives a much lower standard of maintenance than one carrying a passenger service. (*Author*)

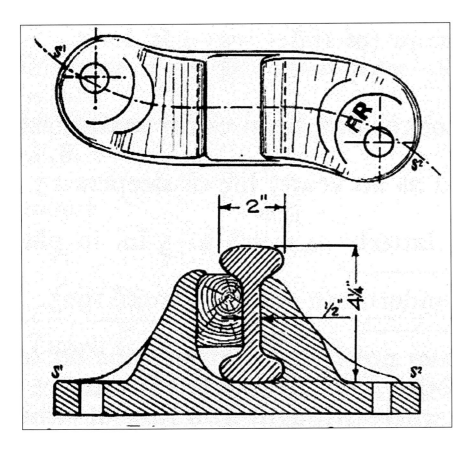

Fig. 65. S-shaped chair, 1868, from the Ffestiniog Railway, weighing 15½lb. (*Author's collection*)

When designing chairs, the opportunity was taken to cant rails inwards, as shown in Fig. 16. This reflected the fact that rolling stock tyres were slightly coned, and so on a straight the train would run along the exact centre of the track, without the flanges touching either rail. Both wear and oscillation from side to side were reduced, thus giving a smoother ride. It also reduced the rolling resistance of the train, and made the locomotive's task easier.

In each chair, the rail was held against one side, usually but not always the inside, by a wooden (generally oak) wedge called a key. The Southern Railway pioneered the use of keys made from spring steel, and these were just as successful. Keys tended to work loose, so replacing and driving them home was one of the lengthmen's tasks. The keys were driven in in the direction of traffic: the rails tended to move in this direction (a phenomenon called 'rail creep') and so helped to hold the keys in place. On curves, however, the outside rail sometimes tended to creep backwards, and again the keys were driven in in such a way as to use this phenomenon to keep them in place.

Before the general adoption of flat-bottomed rails, it had become widespread practice to drill sleepers and fit chairs at central permanent way depots, so that a time-consuming and arduous task could be performed by mechanical means. The sleepers, already chaired, could be delivered to site, and the permanent way gang could then remove life-expired sleepers and replace them with the chairs already *in situ*. From this it was but a short step to making up complete panels of track for speedy installation.

Underbridges needed special care. The consequence of a derailment followed by a fall of many feet can be imagined. Accordingly, several railways added special guard rails, and this occasionally needed a special chair. The Great Central Railway, for example, used one that weighed 93lb.

Cast chairs usually bore the initials of the manufacturer and/or the name of the owning company; sometimes the railway company, for example the London & North Western, manufactured its own chairs.

In the nineteenth century it was usual for chairs to be secured to sleepers by two wrought-iron spikes, but from the 1870s the spikes were supplemented by compressed-oak pegs termed trenails. By the turn of the century many railways were using chairscrews or throughbolts with ferrules as fastenings. The chairscrew, which can still often be seen, had a squared head and was driven in (or removed) by a box spanner with a T handle. Two men could (usually) develop enough force to do the business.

When the installation of flat-bottomed rails became policy in Britain after nationalisation, a great variety of fastenings were tried. In 1964 the Pandrol* fastener was adopted as standard for wooden, concrete and steel sleepers. In recent years, with the spread of continuously welded rails, concrete sleepers have gained favour; the rail baseplate is cast as an integral part of the concrete sleeper, and an insulating pad is laid on it. The rail goes down, two more plastic insulators are inserted, and the Pandrol clip is driven home with two or three blows from a sledgehammer. Once driven into place, the clips will not come out – unless driven out – and will resist rail creep.

We should now consider how rails are joined together to form a continuous surface so that a railway vehicle can run without interruption over vast distances. In the beginning, there were many weird and wonderful methods of accomplishing this. Interlocking rails have been considered above (see Fig. 8). Then came the idea of placing the two rail ends in a common chair, and securing them with a single key. This

---

Whilst flat base plates were most common for flat-bottomed rails, chairs were sometimes used. The Talyllyn Railway, prior to the establishment of its Preservation Society in 1950 (and for quite a few years after), was a case in point. The flat-bottomed rail was held in a chair by a wooden wedge. Your author recalls working on such track in the 1950s. We were lifting it prior to resleepering, and at first we carefully knocked out the keys and unspiked the chairs; then we lifted out the rail and placed the chairs in a wagon body for subsequent sale as scrap. But we soon discovered that if the chair were given a hearty blow from a sledgehammer, it would break into pieces which could be removed much faster – and it was all going for scrap anyway. So, after we had each taken a chair or two as a memento, we got busy with the sledgehammer.

---

* This fastener was invented by a Norwegian named Pande Rolsen. It was taken up by The Elastic Spike Co., which later changed its name to Pandrol UK Ltd.

Fig. 66. A modern Pandrol rail fastener. The baseplate is spiked to the wooden sleeper, then the rail is laid on the baseplate and secured with the spring clip, which is easily driven in with a sledgehammer. (*Author*)

Fig. 67. Bullhead rail with wooden sleepers. Note the method of joining rails with four-hole fishplates either side of the rail. (*Author*)

method was still in use on the Talyllyn Railway in the 1950s. The disadvantage was that if the key fell out, the rail ends might not line up exactly, with consequent risk of derailment. Most common was the simple fishplate: a pair of steel bars, with (usually) four holes cut in them. This is shown in Fig. 67. In the 1930s the London Midland & Scottish Railway experimented with two-hole fishplates (cheaper but not so sturdy), which were equivalent to the old four-hole fishplates cut in half. Much less common was the six-hole fishplate. A variant was the Spooner & Huddart patent fishplate, which supported the bottom part of the bull-head rail and, with luck, made the whole joint more stable and secure. It was used on the Ffestiniog Railway; C.E. Spooner was the Company's Engineer and Sir Joseph Huddart was a partner in several of his ventures. The rail used

Fig. 68. The Spooner & Huddart
Patent Fishplate. (*The Railway
Engineer*)

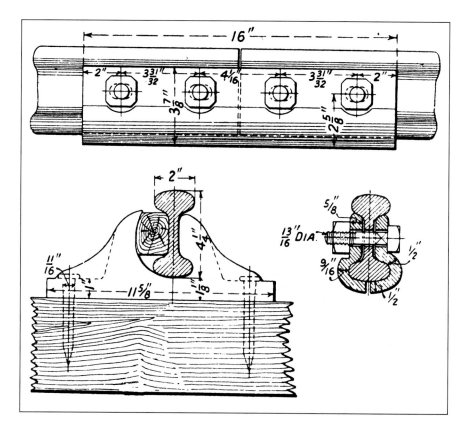

by the Ffestiniog Company at that time was double-headed: that is to say, its top and bottom were of identical section. The intention was that when the top became worn, the rail could be turned and its other side used. As mentioned above, this did not work in practice. Moreover, it was also found that the act of turning the rails threw the fishplate bolt holes out of alignment, and so the whole idea, ingenious as it was, failed.

The fished joint held sway virtually until the end of steam traction on the main lines of Britain and beyond. It can still be seen in sidings and branch lines, and on many secondary main lines. However, it was not long before the idea arose of saving on the cost of fished joints by eliminating them completely. This could be done by welding the rails into a continuous piece. But this presented a problem: what about expansion? Surely the rails would expand in hot sunshine and buckle? This issue was overcome by a number of ingenious devices. One is illustrated at Fig. 71. Here the rails are arranged to slide alongside each other, while presenting a smooth surface to the wheels.

The modern answer to the problem of expansion is that one end of the rail is securely anchored while the other is pulled so that the rail is stretched to the length it would assume in a mean temperature, a process called pre-tensioning. It is then securely fastened down using heavy concrete sleepers more closely spaced than hitherto, with more and better ballast. The great weight of the concrete sleeper, formerly seen as a drawback, is now viewed as an advantage, because it holds the rails down so securely that expansion and contraction are taken up within the great length of the rail itself. The Pandrol rail clip has been

Fig. 69. A Thermit crucible in action. After ignition by a 'sparkler', the bulk of the heat in the crucible is generated by chemical reaction. (*John Moore*)

Fig. 70. After the weld has cooled, the surplus metal around the joint is removed with hammer and set. The set, basically a chisel with a long handle, is being held by the worker on the right while his colleague hits it with a sledgehammer. When most of the surplus metal has been removed, the rail joint will be ground to a smooth profile. This photograph was taken before hi-viz vests became obligatory for men working on track. In more recent years, the hammer and set were replaced by the nitro hammer, and then a hydraulic trimmer, both of which removed the hard labour while speeding up the process and thus reducing line occupancy. (*John Moore*)

Fig. 71. A sliding expansion joint on the Sheffield Super Tram system, at Meadowhall. The two short rails between the running rails are linked to the signalling system and do not make contact with the trams. (*Author*)

found to be the most efficient means of securing the rail and preventing both longitudinal and lateral movement, and is illustrated in Fig. 66.

One might mention here that in the very early days of welding rails – the 1920s and '30s – another problem was identified in the USA: since the weld was of a harder steel than the adjoining rails, when the top surface of the rail became worn the welded joint stood proud. The familiar 'duddity-dun' returned with a vengeance!

But metallurgy moved on. The Thermit process, originally developed in the early 1900s for tramway use and illustrated in Figs. 69 and 70, has enabled welding to be carried out on site. The process consists of clamping a mould around the joint with a funnel-shaped crucible above. This is filled with a mixture of aluminium granules, red iron oxide granules, and steel chippings. The aluminium and red oxide are ignited, and burn with a heat sufficient to melt the steel and allow it to flow down and into the joint. When all is cool, the crucible and mould are removed, and the rail ground down to present a smooth surface to the wheel. This process was initiated in the early years of the twentieth century, but metallurgical developments have resulted in its widespread adoption in comparatively recent years. The advantages of carrying out the welding on site are that fractures can be cut out and fresh rail put in with minimal interruption to traffic. Also, rail, which is manufactured in pieces of 120 feet, can be united into lengths of up to a mile or more – imagine manufacturing a rail 1 mile long, and then moving it to the site of installation!

SIX

ALONG THE TRACK

The observant traveller will notice quite a number of lineside features, of which mileposts and gradient posts are probably the most obvious. Mileposts have been present since the earliest days of railways and they are required by law. Parliament ordered their introduction so that the distance travelled would be clearly apparent to all, and since fares were based on journey length, the passenger would have a measure of protection against overcharging.

In addition, mileposts are useful from the railways' point of view. A spot along the track can be located to within a quarter of a mile by reference to the mileposts. Guards and drivers (and enthusiasts) can measure the time between mileposts and thus calculate the speed of the train.

The earliest mileposts were not unlike those used on eighteenth-century roads, a number of which have survived. On the railways, mileposts of cast iron, and latterly of concrete, became the rule. Zero is the relevant London terminus in the case of main lines, or the junction in the case of branch lines. Miles and the quarter miles are shown by a system of markings. Incidentally, they are usually set on the up side of the line. Mileposts must be clearly visible and legible from a moving train.

Fig. 72. A modern quarter-mile post. (*Author*)

So, while the miles are given in figures, the quarter miles are sometimes indicated by up to three dots or dashes. Fig. 72 is a good example. It is in concrete.

Over the years, the old companies developed their own standard designs. These can often be identified, and serve to show the interested observer which railway company owned the line prior to 1923.

More general notices followed the usual cast-iron format. The example illustrated in Fig. 74 comes from Ropley, and was installed by the London & South Western Railway. Notice that, as a result of repainting by its new owners after the 1923 amalgamation, only the letters S R have been highlighted. Waste not, want not!

Gradient posts show whether the line is level and indicate the severity of the gradient. Changes in gradient are also shown. Such information was vital for guards of loose-coupled freight trains, with only the locomotive and the brake van available to prevent runaways down hill. Gradient posts are

Fig. 73. Some types of mileposts. (*Author*)

Left: Fig. 74. An L&SWR sign turned into an SR one by judicious application of the paintbrush! (*Author*) *Right:* Fig. 75. Gradient post, Southern Railway. In this example, at Ropley Station on the Mid-Hants Railway, there is a change of gradient. Falling from left to right, the gradient steepens from 1 in 250 to 1 in 80. (*Author*)

occasionally made of wood, but more durable materials are usually found, such as the concrete example shown in Fig. 75 from the Southern Railway.

Boundary posts were set up to mark exactly where railway property began and ended. These are sometimes covered in undergrowth now and can be quite difficult to find. More prominent were notices at level crossings and bridges exhorting the public not to trespass on the railway or commit other offences. Occasionally made of wood, they were more commonly cast iron. The usual penalty for transgression was 40 shillings (£2), but some early examples threatened penal servitude, and even transportation to the Antipodes! In Wales, it was not uncommon to find bilingual notices. These were not in response to latter-day pressure from Welsh language enthusiasts,

> The author recalls an embankment near Wanborough, Southern Railway, which showed signs of slipping. A temporary speed restriction was imposed. Enormous quantities of ashes and cinders were dumped on the embankment sides, which continued to slip and spread. The 'temporary' restriction was in place when the author, as an eleven-year-old schoolboy, started travelling regularly by train to and from school. It was still in place when he left school seven years later. Truly, nothing endures like the temporary!

The usual procedure to prevent runaways was to crawl over a summit and stop. The guard walked along the train and manually applied the brakes on the individual wagons. The train then crawled down to the foot of the gradient, where a further stop was made for the brakes to be released. The object was to avoid a sudden snatch on the couplings, which would occur if the train ran downhill unbraked (assuming the train crew remained in control, which sometimes they did not). A snatch could break a three-link coupling, or even a drawbar. With the train divided, the risk of a serious accident was considerably heightened.

There was another way of dealing with the situation but this was frowned on by officialdom. This was to run the train downhill faster than the wagons would run if solely propelled by gravity – and to keep going up the next hill so that the couplings remained taut throughout. So long as there was no sudden emergency requiring a stop – such as a signal unexpectedly at danger – and everyone's nerve held, it worked quite well. As a child living close to the Southern at Sandhurst Halt in the 1940s and '50s, I lay in bed at night and heard freight trains hurtle through at a much faster speed than they ever did in the daytime!

Fig. 76. A Midland Railway boundary post. The head is welded to a short piece of bull head rail. (*Author*)

but date from years when quite a large number of people simply did not speak English, and the railway company needed to communicate with them.

Speed restrictions are imposed for a variety of reasons. Some are permanent, for instance in an area where mining subsidence is to be expected. Some are temporary, such as where the track has recently been worked on and needs time to resettle. Fig. 78 shows the signs used to show the commencement ('C') and termination ('T') of the length of track affected. The driver will, of course, have been given prior warning at his starting depot; he is not expected to bring a 350-ton train down to 15mph at the drop of a hat!

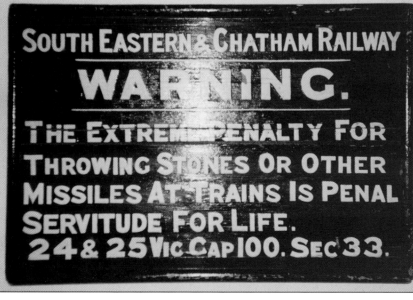

Fig. 77. You have been warned! (*Author*)

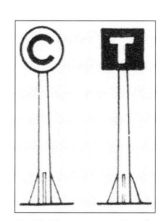

Fig. 78. 'Commencement' and 'Terminates' signs for temporary speed restrictions. (*Author's collection*)

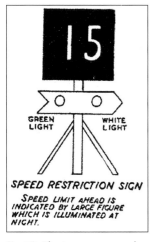

Fig. 79. The temporary speed restriction sign. The arrow points to the track affected. (*Author's collection*)

Fig. 81. A typical 'Whistle' notice. Just out of sight round the curve is an overbridge, and also a footpath crossing the line on the level. A pedestrian would not see a train until it was on top of him. The flat-bottomed rails are fastened to concrete sleepers with Pandrol clips. The distant signal is fixed permanently at danger, to indicate to drivers that they should slow down for a passing loop. The formation originally held double track; the Yorkshire Dales Railway reinstated a single track when it reopened the line. (*Author*)

Fig. 80. An example of a London & North Eastern Railway speed limit sign, which was adopted as standard by British Railways. (*Author*)

Fig. 82. The modern equivalent of the 'Whistle' notice in Fig. 81. This is at Ribblehead station. Here there is a good view up and down the line; trains whistle to alert any would-be passengers. (*Author*)

The London & North Eastern Railway used speed restriction signs that showed the permitted speed in cut-out metal figures, and an example is sketched in Fig. 80. This type of sign was adopted as standard by British Railways in the '50s.

There are many places where a warning blast on the locomotive whistle does not go amiss. The example shown in Fig. 81, on the Yorkshire Dales Railway, is before a curve to the left, in a cutting, followed by an overbridge and a footpath crossing the line on the level.

When someone asked George Stephenson what would happen if a cow strayed onto the track, he is said to have replied: 'It would be the worse for the coo!' Since the earliest days, Parliament has required railways in this country to be adequately fenced to prevent livestock straying onto the line. The observant traveller will notice that the nature of fencing changes according to the location and the materials most readily available: in the northern fell country dry stone walls are not uncommon, while wooden or concrete posts, with wires held apart by galvanised spreaders, are often seen elsewhere. In parts of Wales, some fencing consists of slate slabs wired together. In urban areas brick walls, built high enough to discourage youngsters from straying onto the lines, are common. Wire fences in rural areas often have to be made cattle proof and are frequently reinforced by hedges.

Sheep seem to be especially good at getting through fences and onto tracks. On the Talyllyn Railway, drivers and train staff have developed considerable expertise at dealing with these animals. Turning the cylinder drain cocks on, or throwing coal at them, merely has the effect of causing them to run along the track ahead of the train. It is necessary for the fireman to get down and perform an outflanking move! But on at least one occasion a driver has miscalculated, with tragic results for the sheep. The carcass then disappeared into the firebox, and the smell of roast lamb wafted over the countryside from the locomotive's chimney.

Fig. 83. A watchman's hut near Farnborough North station, where the Southern Region main line to Basingstoke and the West passed over the Guildford to Reading line, the tracks of which are just visible in the foreground. The 'Battle of Britain' class Pacific is heading an up van train in 1954. (*Author*)

Fig. 84. A platelayers' hut at Garsdale. It seems to have had a fire at some time in the past. (*Author*)

Although signalling is outside the scope of this book, we might give a sideways glance to the accommodation provided for fogmen. The task of a fogman was to observe a given signal, if necessary by climbing up the ladder to the top of it, and when it was at danger he placed a detonator on the rail. When the signal was at clear, he removed the detonator. The explosion caused by the train passing over the detonator told the driver that the signal, obscured by fog, was at danger. Such a hut is illustrated in Fig. 83. Normally, a brazier of red-hot coals would be provided to keep the fogman in some semblance of comfort.

We might also briefly consider another type of lineside building which is now fast disappearing: the platelayers' hut. An example is shown in Fig. 84, photographed at Garsdale. It has seen better days, but the basic structure is still clear: a timber shed, well creosoted or tarred, and with a brick-built chimney. Its purpose is obvious from the name: somewhere for the lengthmen to store their tools in safety and out of the weather, and also a place where they could dry themselves and enjoy something hot to eat and drink. Taking alcoholic drinks on duty has only become an offence for railwaymen of all grades in comparatively recent times. Rather like motor vehicle drivers, a railwayman could formerly only be disciplined for being the worse for drink – a subjective assessment.

Telegraph posts were once an indispensable part of the railway scene, but nowadays they have vanished along with so much else. They are shown in several of the illustrations in this book and served not only the railways' own telegraph and telephone network, but also the General Post Office system. Since railways followed much more direct routes across country than roads (alongside which the GPO telephone lines were also a common feature), it made sense to rent lines out to the GPO. Valuable extra revenue was earned from this source. Incidentally, it was a tradition that the arms on telegraph posts were always fixed to the side of the post facing London.

By and large, railway companies did not regard themselves as philanthropic organisations and expected their employees to arrange their own living accommodation. The main exception to this was provision for stationmasters, who were on call 24 hours a day. The stationmaster's house was usually integrated with the station building. When railways came to be built through desolate and uninhabited places, there were no houses already in existence and so the companies built homes for their junior staff, especially signalmen and platelayers. A good example is the Midland Railway's Settle and Carlisle line, which still exists (just), and in much the same state as when it opened in 1876. The railway passed within 5 miles of the market town of Hawes, which had already been

Fig. 85. This is Garsdale – all of it! The settlement consists of the railway station, the platforms of which can be seen to the right of the photograph, and the Midland Railway cottages for the staff. (*John Moore*)

Fig. 86. A closer view of the Midland Railway cottages at Garsdale, seen from the station platform. (*Author*)

reached by the North Eastern Railway with a branch from Northallerton. So the MR threw off a branch of its own, to make an end-on junction with the NER at Hawes. The MR junction was named Hawes Junction, and, because it was truly in the middle of nowhere, the Midland built some cottages for station staff. To this day, apart from the station, they remain almost the sole signs of civilisation in the area. The station was later renamed Garsdale after the valley of the River Clough, a local feature. The branch to Hawes and beyond has been closed and dismantled, and

Fig. 87. It was a very foggy day, and the photograph I took was much too poor for reproduction here, but this somewhat home-made notice was too good to miss!

Fig. 87. It was a very foggy day, and the photograph I took was much too poor for reproduction here, but this somewhat home-made notice was too good to miss!

> # RAILWAY EXECUTIVE
> # SHOOTING, FISHING AND
> # EGGING PROHIBITED
> # BY ORDER

Garsdale station now has the status of an unstaffed halt. A recent photograph of some of the cottages is reproduced here (Fig 86). Observation along the line will reveal quite a number of houses of a very similar design, which were also built by the Midland. Not all are at stations; several are at very remote locations indeed. The two-storey terrace type is the most common, and the double-sided projecting porch, serving two houses, is most characteristic.

Another railway that built houses for its staff was the pioneering Stockton & Darlington. It numbered its houses much as a railway might number its locomotives, and each house bore a number plate. These plates were plain rectangular iron castings. In recent years they have become collectors' pieces and are not so easily spotted as they used to be. Also, the S&DR purchased houses that were sometimes quite a distance from the actual railway, and did not develop a standardised architectural style as the Midland did. Of course, all are now in private ownership.

Many other railways provided houses for staff whose jobs demanded more than usual attention to duty. Examples were shedmasters, who were expected to be on call 24 hours a day, and for whom housing was built or otherwise provided very close to locomotive depots. Even when the depot was situated in a large town, the shedmaster's house was invariably within a few minutes' walk. The provision of 'tied' accommodation reminds us of one aspect of life in the railway service: staff could be, and often were, expected to transfer to a fresh location with only a few days' notice. For staff with children at school, this could be a cruel dilemma, since resigning from the railway service in order to stay in a locality meant finding a new home as well as a new job.

SEVEN

CIVIL ENGINEERING

The civil engineering covered in this chapter needs to be defined a little. The bridges on railways in Britain range from a simple drainage culvert to those spanning the Forth and the Tay, and tunnels vary from less than 100yds in length to the Channel Tunnel at over 30 miles. Clearly a variety of conditions have been encountered during their construction. There are many books dealing with the larger and more dramatic bridges and tunnels and it is not proposed to go over this ground again; the interested reader is referred to other works for this information.* Here it is proposed to cover earthworks for ordinary cuttings and embankments; shorter tunnels; viaducts of various materials; under- and over-line bridges; and opening bridges.

Although it is perfectly possible to lay track on unprepared ground, most railways are laid on a prepared surface in order to effect drainage, ease gradients and maintain as straight a course as possible. It will be observed that land is seldom smooth and level – apart from in such exceptional circumstances as those prevailing on the Nullarbor Plain in Australia, where the track is laid on the ground, dead straight and flat for over 300 miles. Generally, to effect a smooth surface for rails, cuttings

Fig. 88. Preparing to lay track on level ground at Bolton Abbey station, Yorkshire Dales Railway. The excavator is levelling a layer of gravel, on top of which will come the ballast, and then the track panels. The job being undertaken is simply to extend the siding, the end of which can be glimpsed at the right of the picture. (*Author*)

* For a racy but fascinating account of the first Tay Bridge, see *The High Girders*, by John Prebble (Martin Secker & Warburg, 1956).

Fig. 89. A few weeks after the previous photograph was taken, the track bed has been completed, a layer of ballast laid, the sleepers placed in position, and one bull-head rail has been mounted in chairs. The alignment will probably be improved by slewing the track into a smoother curve, but, since the track is only a siding, I cannot be certain about this. More ballast will be added, level with the tops of the sleepers. (*Author*)

and embankments have to be formed. In addition, curves are made as gentle as possible; a curve on a main line railway will be struck on a radius of several miles. All this means that before the track is laid, a good deal of civil engineering must take place.

In the eighteenth century and earlier, 'engineers' constructed fortifications for military purposes. They dug trenches and constructed earthworks for artillery protection. As such, they were the ancestors of the present Corps of Royal Engineers. Once such work became general for civil purposes, such as canals, roads and railways, the engineers involved needed to differentiate themselves from the military. They called themselves 'civil engineers', and the expression gained common currency.

In constructing a railway, the formation is built first. Today (e.g. on the East Coast main line bypassing Selby) it is done by earth-moving machines, but the formations of most of Britain's railways were built by hand by navvies with picks, shovels, wheelbarrows and horses. These included cuttings, embankments and tunnels. A nineteenth-century view is reproduced in Fig. 94. The sloped plank barrow-runs can be seen on the cutting side. When each navvy had filled his wheelbarrow, he attached it to a rope at the foot of the barrow-

Fig. 90. The Causey Arch, sometimes called the Tanfield Arch, County Durham. Built in 1726 for a horse-operated wooden railway, it is the oldest railway bridge in the world. (*NMPFT/Science & Society Picture Library*)

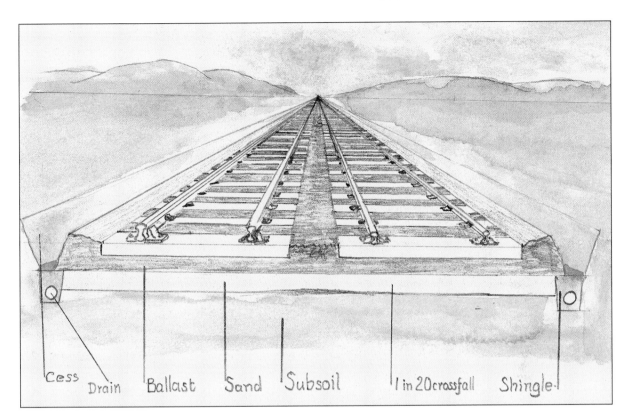

Cess | Drain | Ballast | Sand | Subsoil | 1 in 20 crossfall | Shingle

Fig. 91. Cross-section of double track, showing the formation. (*Author*)

Fig. 92. The new formation of the Great Central Railway's London Extension, looking north from the top of East Leake Tunnel, Nottinghamshire, *c.* 1897. The embankment is constructed from the spoil from the tunnel and cuttings. (*Leicestershire Museum Arts and Records Services*)

run. The top end of the rope was tied to a horse. The horse pulled the barrow up the plankway, with the navvy effecting guidance. If he slipped, or if the barrow fell off the plankway, he would fall to the bottom with the wheelbarrow and its contents coming down on top of him. He risked severe injury or death.

EMBANKMENTS

Wherever possible, the spoil from cuttings and tunnels was used to construct embankments, see Fig. 92. The nature of the soil being worked determined the angle of embankment and cutting sides. This is the science of soil mechanics. Quite clearly, a cutting built through solid rock can have almost vertical sides and Fig. 93 shows excavation work in 1837 at the Olive Mount Cutting, Liverpool. It was cut through red sandstone and is 100ft deep in places. It has been widened over the years, and now accommodates four tracks. As can be seen, the sides are almost vertical. Conversely, a cutting through clay will have gently sloping sides to minimise the risk of the earth slipping down onto the track. The same is true of embankments, although vertical-sided examples are very rare – there are one or two on the narrow-gauge Ffestiniog Railway which resemble dry-stone walls with the track laid along the top, see Fig. 98. The material forming an embankment must be firmly compacted, since it has to withstand the concentrated weight of locomotives and rolling stock, and also the stresses set up by their passing at speed.

In the early days, soil mechanics was little understood and instead formations were constructed by trial and error. If an embankment or a cutting slipped, it was widened. A great deal was learned the hard way, and even today understanding soil mechanics is something of an art. A major problem facing George Stephenson was how to carry the Liverpool & Manchester Railway across Chat Moss. The bog was said by locals to be bottomless, but Stephenson realised this could not be true. So he tipped in spoil, more spoil, and still more spoil, until at last an embankment began to rise above the surface. Where an embankment was not required, he floated the railway on a raft of heather and brushwood. These materials were required in considerable quantities, but Stephenson eventually confounded the sceptics.

On top of the formation comes the ballast. This is in two layers. First hardcore, composed of relatively large pieces of stone extends the whole width of the formation. It allows rainwater to drain away into the formation but not undermine it. On top of this come small granite chippings. These are packed around the sleepers, and have two purposes. First, they prevent the sleepers moving and thus upsetting the alignment of the track, and secondly they aid drainage. Other materials have been tried. The North Eastern Railway used ashes for many years, without ill effects. Furnace slag has been used and at one time the South Eastern Railway and the London, Brighton & South Coast Railway ballasted their track with shingle from the beaches at Dungeness, Newhaven and other places on the south coast. This ballast was reasonably satisfactory for tracks carrying small, light locomotives and trains, but it could not withstand the sideways thrusts of larger and heavier locomotives running at higher speeds. The pebbles were virtually round, and this technique has been likened to ballasting the track with ball bearings! Granite chippings from Meldon Quarry on Dartmoor are ideal for the purpose. They were used by the London & South Western Railway and its successor the Southern Railway, and are still used today.

Fig. 93. Olive Mount Cutting, Liverpool, Liverpool & Manchester Railway. Aquatint coloured by hand, drawn and engraved by T.T. Bury, 1831. (*NMPFT/Science & Society Picture Library*)

Fig. 94. The construction of Tring Cutting, 17 June 1837. (*NMPFT/Science & Society Picture Library*)

Fig. 95. Shingle ballast was quite satisfactory with trains like this – Clapham Junction in about 1900, with D1 class 0–4–2T No. 251 *Singleton* leaving on a down train. But notice how the ballast is brought up over the tops of the sleepers. (*LCGB/Ken Nunn Collection*)

Fig. 96. And shingle ballast was just about acceptable for trains like this – London, Brighton & South Coast Railway, B2 class 4–4–0 No. 201 *Rosebery* passing Streatham on 9 June 1900 before the line was quadrupled. (*LCGB/Ken Nunn Collection*)

Fig. 97. But shingle ballast was certainly not capable of dealing with locomotives as heavy as this! – rebuilt 'Battle of Britain' class 4–6–2 No.34052 *Lord Dowding* near Wilton with an up West of England train, 1957. (*Author*)

Fig. 98. An embankment on the Ffestiniog Railway, constructed of stone, summer 1970. It is in effect a dry stone wall with track laid along the top. (*Ivo Peters*)

In the mid-nineteenth century it was the custom on some railways to bring the ballast almost up to the tops of the rails, completely covering the sleepers and the rail fastenings, see Fig. 95. This gave a solid permanent way, but the gangers found it virtually impossible to check that keys were correctly in place, that sleepers were in good order and that chairs were secure. The Board of Trade remarked on these problems, and eventually the practice of bringing the ballast up to level with, but no higher than, the sleeper tops became almost universal.

Clay subsoil tends to work up through ballast and impede drainage. This causes a rapid deterioration in the track, and there is little that can be done to mitigate the effect. It is usually necessary to lift the track, remove the ballast and hardcore, and renew the lot. Prevention is better than cure: a 'blanket' of layers of gravel, sand, ashes, cinders or crushed rock is inserted between the formation and the ballast. In some cases blocks of concrete have been used, and in the very worst instances the whole formation has been concreted over.

An interesting problem of soil stabilisation occurred in 1949 at Waddesdon, on the former Great Central Railway north of Aylesbury. A soft clay formation in a shallow cutting resulted in heaving of the cesses and 6ft way, and made the sleepers rise. A speed restriction of 50mph was imposed. The clay, in thicknesses of up to 6ft, surmounted a layer of soft oolitic limestone not more than 9in deep. Below this, the Kimmeridge

clay presented a firm foundation. Removal of the top layer of clay down to rock level and its replacement with sand was dismissed as too expensive. Instead holes were driven between the sleepers using a 9in steel spud to a depth of 5ft or down to the limestone, whichever was the less. The resulting hole was filled with sand. Drainage was renewed in the normal way, with precast concrete channels. The result was a complete cure.

Fig. 99. Trackwork on a minor railway. This is the Colne Valley & Halstead Railway, at Colne Valley Junction on 29 July 1911. The ballast covers the middle of the sleepers, but the ends are uncovered. The stability of the track against sideways thrust would be limited, but as long as locomotives were no heavier than that shown and speeds were moderate, it would be acceptable. (*LCGB/Ken Nunn Collection*)

CUTTINGS

The width of cuttings can vary according to circumstances. As already noted, a cutting through rock may have almost vertical sides, while one through clay needs sides of a much gentler slope to avoid landslides in wet weather that might bury the track. Sometimes, however, cutting sides are reinforced by retaining walls, usually of brickwork, see Fig. 102.

Fig. 100 shows a cross-section of a typical cutting. Without the aid of retaining walls, the total width of the cutting would be the distance from C to D – obviously wider than A to B, which is the cross-section when retaining walls are employed. In open country, it is cheaper to buy more land and avoid the need to build and maintain retaining walls, but in an inner-city area, where land is much more expensive, there is every incentive to make the cutting as narrow as possible. Brentwood cutting, on the Great Eastern Railway's main line out of Liverpool Street station, was originally what we might call, referring to Fig. 100 for a moment, a

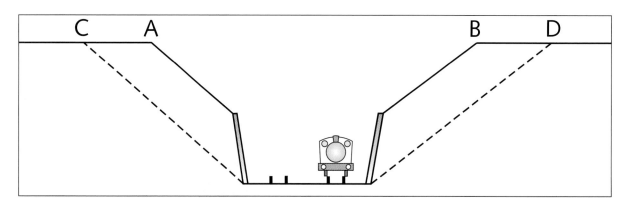

Fig. 100. Cross-section of a typical cutting.

Fig. 101. Brentwood Cutting as originally built. Cut through the London clay, the gently sloping sides will be noted, and also the rural nature of the scene. The train is a down Yarmouth express, the locomotive, No. 1813, is in grey livery, and the date is 6 August 1910. (*LCGB/Ken Nunn Collection*)

'CD' cutting, and was built in a rural area to accommodate two tracks. But by the time the railway had become so busy that it was necessary to quadruple the track, the built-up area had reached the sides of the cutting, so it could not be widened at the top. Retaining walls were employed to support the cutting sides to their original width, while the bottom of the cutting was widened to accommodate the extra tracks.

An unusual solution to the problem of a cutting in ground liable to slipping is the retaining wall with flying arches. Here, the retaining walls are braced by flying buttresses from side to side to resist the inward pressure of the soft soil. The idea was carried a stage further during the construction of the Inner Circle line in London, with what is known as 'cut and cover' tunnelling. A cutting is excavated with vertical retaining walls, and is then roofed over. The Inner Circle was built largely under streets which were closed and then excavated; sewers, water mains and other services were diverted, retaining walls built and a roof installed, and the street reinstated over the top. The railway was originally steam operated, and vents for smoke and steam can still be seen in Charing Cross Gardens on the Embankment. The author, in his early twenties at the time, explained their purpose to a puzzled girlfriend one lunch time, and was promptly put down as a know-all!

TUNNELS

Tunnels have a long history. The earliest (for rail use) date back to horse traction and wooden rails, the longest of which were over a mile. The actual process of excavation has been recounted many times, especially with regard to such epics as the Severn, Woodhead, Standedge and Kilsby tunnels, for example, and the interested reader is referred to the relevant works.

Most tunnels were dug by hand. Navvies armed with picks and shovels, aided by horse power and gravity, and occasionally by steam cranes and winches, dug towards each other. Rock was blasted with black powder, and later dynamite. Timber shoring was inserted immediately behind the miners, who were followed by the bricklayers. Tunnels were usually lined with brickwork – very rarely was a tunnel cut through solid rock and left unlined. Indeed, the only example the present author can recall is Box Tunnel, built by Brunel for the Great Western – and only part of it was left unlined. The brick lining is usually four courses thick, arched at top and bottom and with curved sides. This design resists earth movements. The curved bottom is, of course, filled with ballast so that the track can be laid on a more or less level surface.

Fig. 102. An example of a cutting with retaining walls. This is Marsh Lane, Leeds. The retaining walls enable a four-track line to be built through an inner suburban area using the minimum amount of land. Unfortunately, the cutting sides are used by the residents of the area as a rubbish tip. (*Author*)

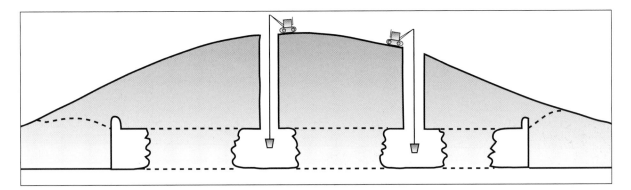

Fig. 103. Excavating a tunnel, and illustrating how the sinking of one or more shafts opens up more working faces.

Mountfield and Wadhurst tunnels, on the South Eastern line from Tonbridge to Hastings, were supposed to have linings four brick courses thick. The line had been opened in 1851, but less than eleven years later it was reported that the lining of Wadhurst Tunnel was bulging. When repairs were made, it was found to have only a single layer of brickwork. The contractors, Messrs Warton & Warden, had been paid for four, and had effectively defrauded the railway company. Extra linings had to be inserted in both tunnels, which reduced their bores accordingly. Thus locomotives and rolling stock were limited to a width of 8ft and had to be specially constructed to work the line. This problem was only solved with electrification in comparatively recent years, when the line through the tunnels was singled. An interesting footnote to this rather disgraceful episode is the inscription to be seen for many years on French and other European goods wagons that came across the channel on train ferries. Amongst the foreign-language markings on them, the following words stood out:

NOT TO WORK BETWEEN TONBRIDGE
AND HASTINGS VIA BATTLE.

Tunnels are, with one or two exceptions, laid out either on a gradient, or with a summit inside. This is to permit drainage. Whilst some are dry, it is not uncommon to see a small stream flowing out of a tunnel mouth. A tunnel will act very much like a well, in that water will collect in it, if measures are not taken to effect drainage. One exception to the drainage rule is at Standedge, which parallels the canal tunnel of the same name on the Huddersfield Narrow Canal. The railway tunnel drains into the canal. Since this was the only stretch of level track on the trans-Pennine route between Manchester and Leeds, the opportunity was taken to lay water troughs in the tunnel – a unique situation. Another exception is the Severn Tunnel, which falls to a point 50ft below the bottom of the estuary from either side. It is only kept from flooding by permanent pumping out of both salt water from the estuary and fresh water from a source named the Great Spring. At 7,666 yards long, or just over 4¼ miles, it was the longest tunnel in Britain for many years, until the construction of the Channel Tunnel – the longest underwater tunnel in the world.

The work of tunnel construction could be speeded up by sinking shafts to the level of the track, and then excavating outwards, as shown in Fig. 103. Some of these constructional shafts were of considerable diameter, and to this day passengers passing through Kilsby Tunnel experience sudden beams of daylight. Smaller diameter shafts were also sunk, initially to get rid of fumes from blasting and then for ventilation. Examples are shown in Figs. 104 and 110. On the surface, such shafts were walled round, and a safety mesh was placed within to deter the curious, the adventurous, the foolhardy and the suicidal. Not all shafts were retained; some were simply filled in once they had served their purpose. In the case of the Severn Tunnel, mentioned above, ventilation shafts are obviously impossible and a 40ft diameter fan was installed to keep it reasonably clear of smoke.

In the days when third-class passengers travelled in open carriages, the prospect of a yawning cavern ahead must have been daunting to say the least, and even the better-heeled passengers would have needed reassurance. As a result, tunnel mouths were constructed on a grand scale for much the same reason that banks have tended to go in for stone architecture – to reassure the nervous about their stability and safety.

It should be borne in mind that engineers were not always free agents who could choose how to finish off a tunnel: local landowners sometimes insisted that a particular style be used to harmonise with his country house. Indeed, some tunnels were built simply because the local landowner insisted the railway be kept out of sight of his residence.

Occasionally a tunnel is wider than appears necessary. Some lines were built to accommodate double track, which in the event was never required, and some were even constructed to take four tracks, which

Fig. 104. A ventilation shaft over Morley Tunnel, near Leeds, seen from the M62. Morley Tunnel, 1 mile 1,609 yards, was begun in 1845 and completed in 1848. (*Author*)

Fig. 105. The castellated entrance to Twerton Tunnel, near Bath, August 1961. The tunnel was built to broad gauge dimensions. (*Ivo Peters*)

Fig. 106. Your author has to admit that he cannot remember where he took this photograph of a tunnel interior some time in the 1950s, from the guard's compartment of an enthusiasts' special train. However, it shows the brick lining, and the smoky conditions that shortened the lives of rails and sleepers. It is thought to be somewhere in the Poole area. (*Author*)

Fig. 107. The Southern main line between Salisbury and Exeter was reduced to single track in 1968. Here the imprint of the down track's sleepers in the ballast can be clearly seen. The train is the 8.50 a.m. Brighton to Exeter, approaching Buckhorn Weston Tunnel. (*Ivo Peters*)

Fig. 108. Mute testimony that the Yorkshire Dales Railway between Embsay and Bolton Abbey was once double track. (*Author*)

Fig.109. The unadorned stone portal of Bincombe Tunnel, near Weymouth, *c.* 1968. Note also the platelayers' cabin behind the first coach. The locomotive, by the way, is 'Battle of Britain' class 4–6–2 No. 34086 *219 Squadron*, and the train is the Sunday 10.12 a.m. from Bournemouth. (*Ivo Peters*)

Fig. 110. A brick portal at Catesby Tunnel, on the old Great Central main line, *c.* 1968. The tunnel mouth has wing walls, and notice the ventilation shaft in the distance. (*Ivo Peters*)

Your author recalls with mixed feelings his one and only acquaintance with the single-line Midhurst Tunnel when he rode on a Pulborough-Midhurst freight. The passenger service had been discontinued a few years previously. Your author was one of a party of enthusiasts who were supposed to be riding in the brake van but, once we were out of sight of authority, half of us transferred to the locomotive. In the forward direction, with the tunnel fitting the train like a glove fitting a finger and the locomotive working hard, those on the footplate resembled smoked kippers on arrival! In the brake van, the windows were coated with sulphurous steam. The tunnel was built on a curve and thus in the middle one could not see daylight in either direction. Your author elected to take his footplate trip on the return journey, when the locomotive was travelling tender first, and thus the cab was ahead of the chimney. The result was as pleasant a passage as could be expected. As one who tends to claustrophobia, your author was very glad of his companions. There is no doubt about it, tunnels are not my favourite locales.

never materialised. It is certainly much cheaper to build earthworks, tunnels and bridges with an eye to the traffic expected to develop than to have to widen them afterwards – and there were plenty of precedents for that – but many lines were built with far too much optimism. In the last quarter of a century or so there has been a good deal of rationalisation. All too often 'rationalisation' means a reduction, and there are new examples of single lines that were once double, and double lines that were once quadruple.

BRIDGES

Underbridges adopted a more or less standard pattern. The rails are laid on longitudinal beams, called waybeams, supported by the main girders. The waybeams had the effect of distributing the load evenly along their length. Gauge was maintained by cross members at intervals of about 6ft.

Long bridges and viaducts were never built on a true curve; each span is straight and the curve is built up from a series of tangents. This is illustrated in Fig. 112, which was photographed from the control end of a push-and-pull train somewhere in the Poole area. It will be seen that the track is laid on a curve, but each steel span is straight. The dips in the girders to rail level indicate the position of the bridge piers.

The through girder bridge shown at Fig. 113, at Battledown, on the Southern Region, is sometimes called an N-girder bridge because of the appearance of the side members. This bridge is built on a skew, and the embankment is supported by a retaining wall.

The timber trestle bridge, at one time widespread in America and familiar to film-goers as a frequent ingredient of Westerns, did appear in Britain. The design was never common, but examples were found on the Lancashire & Yorkshire Railway and the Highland Railway. Some were filled in and converted into embankments, others were rebuilt in other materials, but a very similar structure in steel can still

Fig. 111. A small underline girder bridge crossing a country lane on the freight-only line between Truro and Newham, showing how the rails are laid on waybeams to distribute the load. The two side girders are of different patterns. (*Author*)

Fig. 112. On this single track through truss bridge on the Southern, the deck is solid and normal ballasted track has been laid, but timber baulks have been added outside the rails, to help rolling stock to remain upright in the event of a derailment. (*Author*)

occasionally be found. Dowery Dell viaduct, near Halesowen, is illustrated in Figs. 114 and 115. A severe weight limit was imposed on locomotives permitted to cross it. Fig. 115 shows the decking arrangements, and the very pronounced check rails to prevent derailed rolling stock from turning onto their sides. Fig. 117 shows an extant

Fig. 113. Battledown flyover, Worting Junction, 1957. The up Bournemouth train is passing over the two West of England lines. The down Bournemouth line is immediately behind the camera. (*Author*)

Fig. 114. Dowery Dell viaduct, near Halesowen, in July 1939. LMS 2F class 0–6–0 No. 22579 heads a southbound goods in July 1939. (*H.C. Casserley*)

Fig. 115. Details of the deck of Dowery Dell viaduct. (*H.C. Casserley*)

Fig. 116. The decking of
Meldon Viaduct, on the north
edge of Dartmoor. The rails are
laid on longitudinal waybeams,
with minimal ballast to save
weight. (*H.C. Casserley*)

example on the former Midland Railway's Nottingham to Lincoln line at
Newark.

A special mention should be made of the timber viaducts designed by
Isambard Kingdom Brunel for the West of England and South Wales.
Routes, following a broadly east–west direction, crossed innumerable
steep valleys running north–south, and well over forty viaducts were
built. Some were quite large: at Ivybridge the line was carried 114ft above
the River Erme, and the viaduct at St Pinnock, near Liskeard, was even
higher, at 153ft, while Walkham Viaduct, on the Tavistock line, was
132ft high and 367 yards long. Here masonry piers were topped with a
graceful fan-like timber structure built from yellow pine from Memel in
the Baltic. This was later replaced by Quebec yellow pine, and then
Oregon pine. Brunel's object was economy, and he certainly achieved it.
He developed a design with standard spans of 66ft for the Cornwall and
Tavistock lines, and 50ft for smaller viaducts in West Cornwall. He
designed his viaducts so that any one timber could be removed and
replaced without interrupting traffic. In tidal waters masonry piers were
replaced by timber trestles. But the Oregon pine had a life of only eight
years, which was hopelessly uneconomic in the longer term and as the
need arose for heavier locomotives, the timber viaducts had to go. The last
ones, at Dare and Gamlyn on the Dare branch of the former Vale of
Neath Railway, survived until the line closed on 1 September 1939 and
were dismantled shortly after. Each was 70ft high, and they were 450
and 600ft long respectively. It was said engine crews could feel the Brunel

Fig. 117. Steel trestle bridge carrying the former Midland Railway line over the River Trent at Newark in 1999. The river falls appreciably at this point and passes over a weir. Boats use the lock just visible at the right of the picture. (*Author*)

Fig. 118. A Brunel viaduct near Menheniot, Cornwall, 1957. The piers have been heightened to support a steel deck. (*Author*)

viaducts swaying beneath them, yet the structures suffered no accident or failure.

Replacements for the timber viaducts took one of two forms. In some cases the masonry piers were extended upwards and a deck of steel plate girders was placed across them. In others a completely new viaduct was built alongside. When the second structure was complete, the tracks were slewed onto it and the timbers of the old viaduct were dismantled at leisure. The masonry piers were left standing, and sometimes, covered with ivy, they can still be seen. Other timber viaducts which survive include Barmouth Bridge over the estuary of the River Mawddach. This is 800 yards long.

Trestle viaducts were sometimes made of iron or steel. The Pont y Cafnau tramroad bridge and aqueduct at Merthyr Tydfil, dating from

1793, was probably the world's first iron railway bridge. The crossing for the River Gaunless was built in wrought and cast iron by George Stephenson in 1823 for the Stockton & Darlington Railway, and has been partially re-erected at the National Railway Museum at York. Other notable examples included Belah and Deepdale viaducts on the Stockton & Darlington Railway's extension across the Pennines to Penrith. These were designed by Sir Thomas Bouch, who was also responsible for the ill-fated first Tay Bridge. His Pennine viaducts, opened in 1861, were eminently successful. Belah was 1,040ft long, with a maximum height of 196ft. Deepdale was 740ft long, with a maximum height of 161ft. They both survived until the line was closed in January 1962 and were then demolished. Another example is Meldon Viaduct on the north edge of Dartmoor, which carried the London & South Western Railway's main line from Oakhampton to Plymouth, see Fig. 116. It is still *in situ*, providing access to Meldon Quarries, the source of much of today's railway ballast. The highest was Crumlin Viaduct (1857) in South Wales, which was almost 200ft high. A present-day example of the metal trestle viaduct at Newark is illustrated in Fig. 117.

Just occasionally a bridge over navigable water is required to open to allow shipping to pass. One at Newport, Isle of Wight, consisted of two separate drawbridges, one for each track. Opening either involved dismantling the signal wires! It remained in use up to the closure of the railway, but has since been swept away in a complete redevelopment of the area, which has obliterated almost all signs that a railway was ever there. The more orthodox swing bridge at Turnchapel, Plymouth, illustrated in Fig. 119, must also be referred to in the past tense. Still very much in service is the steel rolling lift bridge illustrated in Fig. 120. This crosses the River Trent at Althorpe, between Doncaster and Scunthorpe, and also carries the A18 road.

Brick and masonry viaducts are commonplace, and your author cannot resist illustrating one of his particular favourites – Ribblehead, on the Midland Railway's Settle and Carlisle line. The viaduct is 1,320ft long, the maximum height is 104ft, and there are twenty-four arches. Although it is sometimes stated that the piers 'were built on wool', this is a reference to the Bradford wool merchants who invested in the railway. In fact, the piers are founded on concrete. Every sixth one was made thicker than its fellows, so that if a pier collapsed, it would only take five with it. A certain romance surrounds this viaduct, and indeed the whole of the Settle and Carlisle line, the Midland Railway's dramatic realisation of its own through-route to Carlisle and Scotland.

Isambard Kingdom Brunel, already mentioned, chose an unorthodox and – since it had not been done before – daring solution to the problem of carrying the Great Western Railway over the River Thames at Maidenhead. He designed a brick bridge with two main spans, each 128ft wide but with a rise of only 24ft 3in. The arches are semi-elliptical. Many people (including some who should have known better) prophesied that it would collapse when the staging was removed. But the bridge stands to this day, having been widened on the original plan to accommodate four tracks instead of two.

Fig. 119. The swing bridge over the River Plym, Plymouth, showing the opening centre span. O2 class 0–4–4T No. 218 approaches Turnchapel with the 12.12 p.m. from Plymouth, 8 July 1924. (*H.C. Casserley*)

Fig. 120. Keadby Bridge, the unusual rolling lift bridge which carries the Doncaster–Scunthorpe railway line and the A18 over the River Trent at Althorpe. (*Author*)

Just occasionally an engineer got his sums wrong. Fig. 122 shows a five-arch bridge near Scunthorpe, which has been strengthened with reinforced concrete beams across the inside of the arches. The arches themselves have also been reinforced. The brickwork shows signs of renewal too. Such reinforcement may have become necessary because of a variety of factors: subsidence in a mining area, insecure foundations in sandy territory or disturbance of the water table can all cause a bridge to

Fig. 121. Ribblehead Viaduct on the Settle and Carlisle line. The viaduct is built of limestone, with brick arches. Although it was constructed to take double track, since 1984 it has carried a single line only. It is built on a curve. (*Author*)

Fig. 122. A bridge carrying the Doncaster–Scunthorpe line of the former Great Central Railway over a road near Scunthorpe. The steel bars, partly made up from old rails, surrounding the right-hand pier suggest that it has been hit by lorries fairly frequently. (*Author*)

subside and need strengthening. There have been several other instances of viaducts collapsing, and a representative selection is discussed in Chapter 16.

The giant viaducts were, of course, the Forth, Tay and Saltash bridges – the latter is illustrated in Fig. 124. These are too familiar to need much comment. The second Tay Bridge is a long viaduct, crossing relatively shallow water, and owes its notoriety to the severe gale that destroyed its somewhat flimsy and ill-constructed predecessor. Similar long steel viaducts crossed the Solway Firth and the River Severn, each bearing a single track. However, the Severn Bridge was overtaken by railway developments. Unable to bear the heaviest main line locomotives, it was not a serious competitor to the Severn Tunnel, though it provided a useful diversion route during repairs. After it was hit by an errant tanker

Fig. 123. The steel viaduct at West Meon, Hampshire, 1955. The photograph was taken shortly after the line closed; the crane was engaged in demolition. (*Author*)

Fig. 124. The Saltash Bridge, seen from the Torpoint Ferry in 1957 and before the construction of the modern road bridge. (*Author*)

in fog on the night of 25 October 1960 and two of its spans were brought down, it was never repaired. It was later dismantled.

Another variant was the box girder bridge. The idea behind it was to produce a wrought-iron girder that would be long enough to cover a sizeable span and strong enough to take a train. Robert Stephenson used the idea for his bridges at Conway and Menai; the boxes are big enough for the train to run inside. In each case two box girders, or tubes, were set side by side, one for each track. At Saltash, Brunel placed his tubes above the track and suspended the deck from them. Saltash Bridge was intended to be double track, but the South Devon Railway directors could not raise enough cash and so Brunel was directed to make it single track, and

Fig. 125. An LMS bridge plate. (*Author*)

single track it remains to this day – the only stretch of single line between Paddington and Penzance.

Bridges were usually numbered, though the Highland Railway knew the ones on its lines by name only. The number, on a cast-iron plate, was prominently displayed and many can still be seen. Plates are usually rectangular or oval, like the LMS plate shown in Fig. 125. Just occasionally bridge numbers were painted on the end of the parapet. The numbers started from zero at the start of each stretch of track. They were not numbered in one all-embracing series – with several thousand to deal with, the system would soon have become unwieldy. As an aside, such plates have become quite popular with collectors of railwayana for use as house numbers.

Depending on the availability of local building materials, most over- and underbridges were of either brick or stone. Such bridges crossing streams and country roads, exist by the hundred. The methods of construction were always similar. The sides, or spandrel walls were erected along with the wing retaining walls at the ends of the embankment. A wooden former was then placed at the top of the inside walls, and the arch constructed on top of it. Once the cement was really dry, the former was removed. The hollow shell of the bridge was then filled with hardcore – a mixture of rubble, stone, gravel, etc. Drainage holes were left at strategic points so that the whole thing would not fill with water when it rained, and the ballast and track were laid on top. Just occasionally a different kind of hardcore would be used: Brackley viaduct on the Great Central Railway was filled with concrete. When the line closed and attempts were made to demolish the viaduct, it was only brought down after explosives were used.

Fig. 126. Bridge No. 171 on the Southern Region West of England main line, somewhere west of Basingstoke, 1956. Incidentally, this photograph gives a good view of a tapering brick-built pier of a high three-arch bridge spanning the railway cutting. (*Author*)

Frequently the bridge would be built on a skew. George Stephenson is said to have constructed the first of the type, at Rainhill on the Liverpool & Manchester Railway, and to have demonstrated the principle by carving a model from a turnip with his knife. Skew bridges call for some careful bricklaying, but no other special techniques.

In more recent years, reinforced concrete has become available as a building medium. The first concrete viaduct of any size was constructed at Glenfinnan on the West Highland Railway in Scotland. The contractor

Fig. 127. A most unusual situation: a viaduct over a bridge. This is Midford Viaduct, on the Somerset & Dorset Joint Railway, with Standard Class 5 No. 73116 on the 11.00 a.m. Bath–Evercreech Junction goods on 30 June 1958. Below, pannier tank No. 9628 stands on the GWR Limpley Stoke–Camerton branch with the demolition train. (*Ivo Peters*)

As a fifteen-year-old schoolboy, and very much into model railways, your author sought the assistance of his maths master: how do I lay out a shape on card which, when cut out and curved, will fit under a model skew bridge? The master replied that it could be done, but it was much too complicated for me to understand. He suggested that I cut a piece of card oversize, glue it in place, and trim away the surplus when the glue had set. This worked very well, and I have since made several skew bridges on various layouts by this method. Many years later, when married to a school teacher, I recounted the above. Patricia let me into a trade secret. She informed me that 'It's much too complicated for you to understand' almost certainly meant 'I haven't the foggiest idea!'

Fig. 128. A plate girder bridge over the main line at Hurstbourne, Southern Region, contrasts with a brick arch over the abandoned formation of the Longparish branch. Note the superb alignment and the neat shoulder to the ballast. (*Author*)

Fig. 129. A skew bridge carrying the Great Northern Railway's line from Leeds to Wakefield over a road in Leeds, and showing how the stone blocks are laid to create a skewed arch. (*Author*)

was Sir Robert McAlpine, who promoted the material's use with enthusiasm, so much so that he was nicknamed 'Concrete Bob'.

Foundations are critical in bridge-building. At Brackley, mentioned above, inverted arches were placed below ground level to tackle the problem of potentially unstable ground. At Bugsworth, on the Midland Railway, a viaduct was built in the 1860s on shale superimposed on sandstone. The shale began to move, taking with it about 16 acres of farmland and a farmhouse, and breaking the Midland Railway's viaduct, which was reconstructed.

The Liverpool Overhead Railway, opened in 1893, was laid on a continuous steel viaduct, and a short section is illustrated in Fig. 131. It was the necessity of renewing most of this viaduct, coupled with the inability of the LOR to pay for it, that forced the railway's closure in 1956.

Fig. 130. This is the easy way to build a skew bridge, especially when headroom is limited. When the London & North Western Railway entered Leeds, a new bridge over the road was built alongside the one shown in Fig. 129: plain abutments and steel girders crossed the gap! Less than a week after this photograph was taken, the bridge was dismantled and comprehensively rebuilt to accommodate a revised track layout. (*Author*)

Fig. 131. The Liverpool Overhead Railway near Pier Head station, 1955, showing the type of steel plate girder viaduct employed, and a bow-string bridge to span a larger opening – in this case, to give lorries access to the docks. (*Author*)

LEVEL CROSSINGS

We have seen that railways crossed roads by means of bridges over and under the track. Level crossings were also very common, but with the growth of road traffic they have become something of a nuisance, both to road and rail. Many have been replaced by bridges, but others remain. The old-fashioned fully gated crossing is now a rarity, and it was necessary to visit a preserved steam railway to take the photograph in Fig. 132. Its modern counterpart is shown in Fig. 133. The gates are replaced by lifting barriers monitored remotely via the closed-circuit television cameras visible in the picture. Originally, the barriers only covered one half of the road, but some motorists were stupid enough to try zig-zagging round them – and got themselves killed in the process. So, to protect motorists from themselves, the barriers now cover both sides of the road, as shown.

The level crossing gates shown in Fig. 132 are hand operated. When a signalbox was adjacent, it was common for the gates to be operated by the signalman, with the aid of a kind of ship's windlass in the signalbox. There were special cases to meet special needs: for example, at North Camp, on the Southern, the gates opened outwards, and there were markings on the road advising traffic to stop well clear of the crossing. Of course, there were occasions when the road markings were obstructed or ignored, and the gates could not be opened unless a line of traffic several hundred yards long could be persuaded to back up.

Fig. 132. The traditional level crossing, with hand-operated gates. This is at Oakworth, on the Keighley & Worth Valley Railway. The train has just passed, and a member of the station staff is opening the gates for the waiting road traffic. (*Author*)

Fig. 133. A modern level crossing at Steeton, near Keighley. The barriers are raised, so there is nothing to prevent children, animals or the foolhardy from venturing onto the track. Just behind the left-hand traffic light are the closed-circuit television cameras that enable the signalman, several miles distant, to see what is going on, even if he is virtually powerless to do anything about it. (*Author*)

Fig. 134. An ungated crossing for a footpath near Honiton Tunnel, Southern Railway, *c*. 1925. The only protection for pedestrians is a notice advising them to 'STOP, LOOK AND LISTEN BEFORE CROSSING THE LINE'. (*H.C. Casserley*)

GRADIENTS AND INCLINES

It is true that early steam locomotives were not good at hill climbing, and George Stephenson and Isambard Kingdom Brunel both preferred a level if circuitous course. But, as the steam locomotive developed, it became possible to tackle more formidable inclines. 1 in 100 became quite an acceptable ruling gradient, and a good example of this is the Settle–Carlisle line built by the former Midland Railway. For short sections, much steeper gradients were accepted, though they were often a bugbear for the railways' motive power departments. Inclines such as the Lickey, near Bromsgrove, at 1 in 37½, the West Coast Main Line climbs at Grayrigg, Oxenholme and Shap, and the climb from Ilfracombe to Morthoe at 1 in 36 (now closed) put a severe strain on locomotives throughout the steam age, and the burden was only eased with the arrival of diesel and electric traction.

I.K. Brunel became enchanted with the idea of atmospheric propulsion, and this has been discussed in Chapter 3 above. One perceived advantage of the system was that gradients no longer mattered. The pressure of the atmosphere could propel trains up the steepest of gradients at speeds, so Brunel averred, of 40 to 50mph. Brunel laid out the South Devon Railway with little regard to gradients and every regard to economy. The result was the formidable banks of Rattery, Hemerdon and Dainton – Dainton was at an inclination of 1 in 42–43 – which the company had to try to work with locomotives. At the end of the 'atmospheric caper', (Robert Stephenson's words) the South Devon had lost about £353,000.

Fig. 135. The limit of adhesion traction? A train approaching the summit of Hopton Incline, Cromford & High Peak Railway, 1934. The gradient at this point is 1 in 14. The usual technique here was to charge the incline. The train would hit the bottom at about 30mph, and would be down to walking pace or less by the summit. Note that, on this mineral line, the train has no brake van. (*H.C. Casserley*)

It was also saddled with a main line with gradients that have been a problem ever since. The usual method of tackling them in steam days was to double-head, but other steep inclines, such as the Lickey, near Bromsgrove, were worked by banking locomotives. The Midland Railway provided the only 0–10–0 tender locomotive Britain has ever seen, especially for the job. Northbound trains would come to a stand at Bromsgrove, and 'Big Emma' would buffer up at the rear. With an exchange of whistles, the cavalcade would set off, the gradient starting virtually at the platform's end. With both the engine and the banker working flat out, the train would be shouldered up to the summit. Whilst the train accelerated away, the banker would drop behind, cross over to the other line and drop down the incline to Bromsgrove to await the next train, when the performance would be repeated.

Such ferocious gradients were, fortunately, of relatively short length. The 1 in 37 climb from Exeter St David's station to the Southern Railway's Exeter Central is half a mile, and on a long sweeping curve with a short tunnel. The usual procedure was for Southern trains to come to a stand at St David's, and for one or two tank locomotives to come on to the rear. Once away, it was the two bankers that did the work, with the train locomotive doing little more than moving itself. A fireman once told me why: 'It's the two bankers who arrive at Central with their

Fig. 136. Super power. A northbound freight tops the Lickey Incline, with 2–10–0 No. 92155 in charge, early 1960s. This photograph shows the quite dramatic change of gradient. The board to the left advises all southbound freight trains to stop and pin down brakes. (*Ivo Peters*)

fires torn to pieces; my fire is in good order to work forward to Salisbury and Waterloo!'

The Worsborough Incline in South Yorkshire was on the mineral branch from Wath marshalling yard to Penistone, and was nominally at 1 in 40. (Mining subsidence meant that in places it was a good deal steeper.) Here the London & North Eastern Railway provided another unique banker: a Beyer-Garratt 2–8–0+0–8–2. The train would be headed by one of the ex-Great Central 2–8–0s which were LNER class O4, and the Garratt would bring up the rear. With both locomotives developing maximum power, the train would march up the incline at little more than walking pace. Consider how much driving skill was necessary to keep those two great locomotives working in perfect unison to avoid coming to a standstill on the incline!

Many other examples could be cited. The 1 in 36 climb from Ilfracombe to Morthoe, the Highland Railway climb from Blair Atholl to Druimachdar . . . but they all added up to bad news for the operating and locomotive departments, and were expensive to operate. The electrification of the West Coast Main Line saw the end of banking from Oxenholme to Shap Summit, and gave rise to such headlines in the railway press as 'Shap Flattened!'. Modern electric power tackled the gradients as if they simply weren't there. The concept of energy generated at a central station powering the trains over steep gradients had returned, and Brunel would have been delighted.

EIGHT

ELECTRIFIED TRACK

T he track used for railways electrified with overhead wires is exactly the same as the permanent way described in foregoing chapters, and so can be ignored for our present purpose. But when trackwork is electrified by the use of conductor rails, then we need to look a little more closely.

THIRD RAIL

The term third rail is generally taken to mean a single conductor rail mounted outside the running rails. The main exponent of this system was the Southern Railway and Southern Region of British Railways, where the electrification eventually covered most of a triangle from London to Dover and Weymouth. The third rail was of a special flat-bottomed cross-

Fig. 137. Southern Railway third-rail electrification. The conductor rail, of flat-bottom section, can be seen mounted on insulating chairs. At this station, Christ's Hospital, there are no wooden guards, but the third rail is kept away from the platform edge. The line leading to the left is the Guildford branch, which was unelectrified. The 23 on the front of the twelve-coach restaurant car express tells us that it is on a London Bridge to Portsmouth Harbour service. A gradient post can be seen to the right of the picture. This photograph was taken in 1953 or 1954. (*Author*)

The third rail was chosen by the Southern Railway (and its predecessor the London & South Western Railway) for reasons of economy: it is much cheaper to install than overhead wires which require frequent supporting gantries. But there are disadvantages. In the first place, it is dangerous for men working on the track and it can be fatal to trespassers – your author has personally heard of two small children killed in this way. Ice and snow interfere with the conductivity and can paralyse services. A further drawback is the gaps in the conductor rail which are inevitable at points and crossings both where one line of track crosses another, and where the railway crosses a road or pedestrian right of way on the level. The Southern sloped the ends of the third rail downwards, and painted them white, while London Transport used special cast conductor rail ends which served the same purpose. When your author was a child, the electrification extended westwards from Brookwood only as far as Sturt Lane Junction, Frimley. The layout is shown in the sketch in Fig. 138. In those days (mid-1950s) there was a service of one or two electric trains per day which passed over the junction on their way from Brookwood to Frimley and thence to Camberley, Bagshot and Ascot. As will be seen from the sketch, trains coming from the Frimley direction could join the main line without difficulty, but trains going from Brookwood to Frimley had to cross a sizeable gap in the third rail. The usual routine was to approach the junction with enough speed to coast over the gap and resume contact on the other side. But it was not unknown for a two-coach train to become 'gapped', and stuck right across the junction, blocking all four main lines. Then a steam locomotive would have to be summoned from Woking to propel the lifeless electric across the junction and so, eventually, resume normal service!

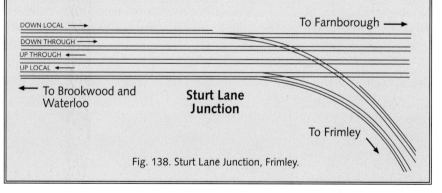

Fig. 138. Sturt Lane Junction, Frimley.

section and mounted in earthenware chairs. In station areas the third rail was often protected by wooden side boards, and kept away from platform edges as much as possible.

The third rail system is not without limiting factors. The fact that a train's pick-up shoes are required to make contact with the rail at rail ends at speed, i.e. to strike the rail at up to 90mph, has had a limiting effect on the speeds that can be attained – 100mph seems to be the maximum for practical purposes, while overhead electric trains reach 140mph and more. A further disadvantage is the number of electricity substations, positioned every few miles, that are required to feed the current at 660 volts DC to the conductor rails. Three-phase alternating

current was generated by the Southern's own power station at Durnsford Road, Wimbledon, at 11,000 volts, 25 cycles. The substations rectified it to direct current and stepped it down by transformers to 660 volts for the trains to use.

Junctions are treated in different ways on a third rail system. Where speeds are relatively low, the shoe can be allowed to slide off the side of the rail if a train is taking a diverging route, with a short ramp fixed to the side of the track. This also serves for use in the opposite direction. Otherwise, there is a short gap at the actual point of divergence.

The vexed question of gaps in the conductor rail has been mentioned at some length, because, for obvious reasons, it could have a profound effect on the operation (or non-operation) of trains. Therefore, although it is strictly outside the scope of this book, it is worth spending a few moments considering how the problem was solved where third rail pick-up shoes could not be distributed along a train, that is with electric locomotives.

The Southern Railway only built two main-line electric locomotives. British Railways added a third in 1948. The collector shoes supplied power to a 600-volt motor, directly coupled to a 600-volt generator fitted with a heavy flywheel. The current from this generator powered the traction motors at the axles. The flywheel stored enough kinetic energy to keep the generator producing electricity and the locomotive developing tractive effort over the longest gaps. The locomotives were even capable of entering a long unelectrified siding and retrieving wagons from the far end. The system was subsequently employed in a series of electric

Fig. 139. An electric express with Pullman car arriving at Brighton in the 1950s. The wooden protectors to the third rail can be seen. Cables connecting the various short sections of third rail are carried in concrete conduits, which can be seen beside the train. Notice that the ends of the third rail slope down, and, together with the ends of the wooden protectors, are painted white. The 4 on the front of the twelve-coach express indicates a London Victoria to Brighton express service. (*Author*)

Fig. 140. This shows the heavy cable for carrying the current to otherwise isolated sections of conductor rail. (*Author*)

locomotives, class 71, built for the Southern by British Railways after nationalisation. These were mounted on eight wheels instead of their predecessors' twelve, and weighed 77 tons as opposed to 99. They developed 2,500hp, compared with 1,470hp of the earlier machines.

The Liverpool Overhead Railway was laid on a continuous viaduct, hence its name. As can be seen from the photograph of Pier Head station reproduced in Fig. 141, the track used sleepers stretching the full width of the double track. The third rail was further away from the running rails than on the Southern or London Transport, and, as can be seen, no form of protection, either at or away from stations, was used. Some LOR trains worked through to Southport over the ex-Lancashire & Yorkshire Railway's electrification.

In the Liverpool area, the Lancashire & Yorkshire Railway inaugurated electric trains to Southport in October 1904. At Seaforth, the northern terminus of the Liverpool Overhead Railway, there was a junction between

Southern electric locomotives were normally used on freight trains, but they did have one regular passenger turn. This was the Newhaven boat express. The story (possibly apocryphal) goes that on one occasion an electric locomotive brought the express up to London without mishap, and was stopped by signals just outside Victoria. The signal cleared, the driver moved his controller, and – nothing happened. He tried again: still nothing. He checked everything, ensured that the locomotive was in contact with the third rail, and made yet another fruitless attempt to start. Eventually a steam locomotive was summoned to propel the train into the station. The passengers were disembarked, the coaches removed, and the lifeless electric locomotive was towed out and put into a siding. The following day, an electrical engineer from Eastleigh arrived to examine it. He climbed into the cab, inserted his key, tried the controller – and away it went! And they *never* found what was wrong with it!

Fig. 141. A train approaching
Pier Head station, Liverpool
Overhead Railway, 1955.
(*Author*)

the two lines, and because their electrification systems were similar, a certain amount of through working was possible. Although the LOR has since closed, the Liverpool–Southport electric trains continue to operate.

The Lancashire & Yorkshire Railway electrified the Manchester to Bury line in 1916 at 1,200 volts DC, using a third rail, unique in Britain, that was boxed in over the top. The train's pick-up shoes pressed against the side of the rail. 1,200 volts was distinctly high – the Southern used 660 volts – but here again there were precedents overseas. The system was extended briefly to Holcombe Brook, although that branch ultimately reverted to steam traction before total closure. The system used track of normal cross-sleeper type, with the conductor rail mounted in chairs at the sleeper end. The original rolling stock continued in use until it was replaced by British Railways in 1959, and the line has since been re-electrified with overhead wires to form part of the Manchester Super-Tram system.

The North Eastern Railway commenced electrification of the Newcastle suburban lines in 1904. South Tyneside electrics were replaced by diesel multiple units in January 1963, and North Tyneside electrics were replaced in 1967.

CENTRE THIRD RAIL

The centre third rail system is very like the electric toy train set of yore, as manufactured by Messrs Meccano for their Hornby series. It is quite

Fig. 142. A car on Volk's Electric Railway, Brighton. The offset centre conductor rail is clearly shown. The photograph was taken in 1953, and the car is decorated for the coronation of Queen Elizabeth II. (*Author*)

rare in this country, and the only example known to the author was the original Central London Railway, now part of the London Underground's Central Line.

There is another centre third rail electric line which must be mentioned, and that is Volk's Electric Railway along the seashore at Brighton. This line, opened in August 1883 and built by Magnus Volk, a local electrical engineer who later illuminated the Brighton Royal Pavilion, is unique, not only for its track gauge of 2ft 8½in, but also for its off-centre third rail shown in Fig. 142. Just why it came to be offset is not known to the author. It means, of course, that the cars cannot be turned. But since the railway has no means of turning its stock, this presents no problem.

FOURTH RAIL

The main exponents of this system are London Transport and the ex-London & North Western Railway electrification in the London area covering the lines from Euston (and Broad Street, before it closed) to Richmond and Willesden Junction. The Mersey Railway, only 4.8 miles long, was steam operated from its inception in 1886 until it converted to electricity in 1903 on the four rail 650 volts DC system. Its associated lines in the Wirral peninsula were electrified by the London Midland & Scottish Railway in 1938 at 650 volts DC, to permit inter-running with the Mersey Railway.

The advantage of the fourth-rail over the three-rail system is that the return current is via the centre rail and thus is kept clear of the running rails. This meant that there were no stray currents to interfere with the

early telephone system, then mostly earth return too. It also released the running rails for track circuits (see below).

The centre, negative, rail is 1½in above the surface of the running rails, while the outside, positive, rail is 3in above. This means that at points and crossings, there is 1½in clearance when a positive collector shoe passes over a negative rail and hence, hopefully, no possibility of a short circuit. The insulators for the outside rail were 1½in higher than those for the centre.

TRACK CIRCUITS

Although not concerned with electric traction, track circuits do require an electric current in the rails, and so might be discussed here. Briefly, the idea was to take advantage of the fact that wooden and concrete sleepers electrically isolated the two rails from each other – apart from at points, of course. If a low voltage electric current were to be arranged so that it would flow from one rail to the other only through the wheels and axles of passing trains, then the presence or absence of a train could be made to show up in the signalbox. From this it was a short step to the presence of a train being the trigger to close the circuit in rear of a signal, returning that signal to danger and clearing it once it had passed out of the section. The drawback to this simple scheme is that the signal is normally at All Clear, and if the system fails then this indication will be given – whether there is a train in the section or not. As a result, this

Fig. 143. This photograph was taken in about 1912 and shows the Ealing line flyover, looking towards Turnham Green. The fourth-rail electrification is clearly visible. Note the treadles on the two tracks to the left, one just before the permanent way gang. The points have a cast-steel crossing. The centre conductor rail ends with a cast-steel rail end incorporating a slope. The electrified tracks belonged to the Metropolitan District Railway; the unelectrified lines to the London & South Western Railway. (*London Transport Museum*)

Fig. 144. Wire has been welded across a rail joint to afford a better path for the return current. This photograph, taken at Alton, Hampshire, in 1999, shows the absence of protective boards and of the earlier habit of painting conductor rail ends white. (*Author*)

scheme has not been too popular, and as a signalling topic it is really outside the scope of this book.

Since the presence of a simple turnout would cause a track circuit to short circuit, the ends of a circuited section of track must be electrically isolated from the track on either side. This is done by installing insulating fishplates made of wood, fibre, or plastic. There must also be insulation between the two ends of the rails to ensure that they do not touch when expansion occurs in hot weather. Similarly, it is generally felt that it is unwise to rely on the normal steel fishplates and bolts to effect an efficient electrical connection, and so the rails are connected by steel wires which are welded onto them. An example is given in Fig. 144.

TEMPORARY TRACK

Railway track is often called the 'permanent way', but before the 'permanent' track goes down, a temporary way is often required. The need to move excavated soil or rock, and other materials, has in the past been met by laying a temporary railway – similar to those used in civil engineering projects like dams. An example is shown in Fig. 145. Notice how the track switchbacks along the proposed route. Contractors' locomotives were recorded as hauling two loaded wagons weighing 23 tons up a gradient of 1 in 9 on a 5 chain curve, and under the most favourable conditions a load of 75 tons had been worked, the latter from the contractor's depot under a nascent viaduct to the track level at the top!

The track itself in Fig. 145 should also be noted, in particular the fact that the light flat-bottomed rail is spiked directly to 'sleepers' cut from rough-hewn timber, and with no attempt at ballasting. Pointwork was often of the stub variety discussed in Chapter 5, but with corners rather than curves! Clearly, speeds were extremely low and derailments frequent.

Fig. 145. A contractor's railway near Rugby on the course of the Great Central Railway's London extension, *c.* 1897. (*Leicestershire Museum Arts and Records Services*)

Fig. 146. An example of a turnout for portable use. This one has been mounted on cut-down main line sleepers for display purposes. The gauge, which here is 24in, could be anything from 18 to 24in. Your author, as a teenager, found the turnout abandoned at the site of a former brickworks, retrieved it and set it up at his parents' home. The straight rails were cut to size by hand, using a hacksaw! Later, a Ffestiniog Railway slate wagon was mounted on it. But all good things come to an end: we moved house, there was no room at the new address, and, alas, the scrap merchants were called in. (*Author*)

Fig. 147. A section of jubilee track preserved at the National Mining Museum, near Wakefield. Note the pressed-steel sleeper. (*Author*)

Smaller projects were at one time served by narrow gauge railways that were temporary in the extreme. This is sometimes termed 'Jubilee' track, and Robert Hudson Ltd, already mentioned in connection with steel rails, was among the firms manufacturing such equipment – track, rolling stock and all the fittings necessary for a complete railway. In France, the Decauville Company produced very similar equipment, which is occasionally to be found on this side of the Channel.

Jubilee track is made up in lengths, with the rails riveted to steel sleepers. The sleepers are at approximately 3ft intervals. Each length of

track can be lifted by two or three men and manhandled into position. Fishplated joints can then be easily and quickly effected, and a temporary track layout promptly established. As operations develop, the track can be dismantled and reassembled into a different layout – not unlike the 'lines' of a child's toy train set. Points were similarly treated, and a specimen is shown in Fig. 146. It will be noted that the tongues, or 'points', of the turnout are loose, though linked together, and the points are set by a well-aimed kick with the boot! (In the example illustrated, the turnout has been slightly modified: a piece of angle iron has been pivoted to the tie bar, so that the point can be set and secured from the end of the track, out of the camera's sight to the left.) Also, note that the whole turnout is mounted on only four sleepers. The author speaks from practical experience in saying that such a set could be carried (a short distance!) by only two men – in the case of the example illustrated, his father and himself.

Fig. 148, reproduced from Hudson's catalogue, shows variations on the theme, including turnouts with switchboxes to make them suitable for locomotives. Derailments of light wagons either pulled by an animal or pushed by a man could easily be righted, but putting a locomotive 'on the

> Talking of derailments, your author recalls an '8F' class 2–8–0 steam locomotive, weighing 72 tons, being rerailed with jacks and packing on a preserved railway in Yorkshire in 1998 in just over two hours.

floor' back onto the rails was a rather more serious operation. However, as long as it had not landed on its side or upside down, rerailing usually called for a jack or two, and several thick baulks of timber, rather than a breakdown crane.

MILITARY TRACK

Slightly outside the scope of this book, but nevertheless worth a mention, is the use made of temporary track by the military in the First World War. Tracks ranged from 'main lines' to the flimsiest of temporary ways at the front line itself – on the 2ft or 60cm gauge.

TEN

TOOLS OF THE TRADE

To refer to tracklaying and maintenance as a 'trade' may seem a little presumptuous, especially as the railways traditionally regarded such staff as unskilled labour – and paid them accordingly. Nevertheless, as, I hope, the preceding pages have demonstrated, there was (and is) considerably more to working on the track than simply walking a length and hitting the occasional key with a sledgehammer.

Laying and maintaining trackwork was originally extremely labour-intensive. The men were expected to look out for themselves, but in several cases of they became so engrossed in their work that they failed to hear the whistle of an approaching train until it was too late. There were also examples of the approaching locomotive failing to whistle, with equally fatal results. And, finally, there have been permanent way men who stepped aside to avoid one approaching train – straight into the path of another. So the Railway Inspectorate insisted on a look-out. He carried flags, and gave warning of an approaching train either with a whistle or by a blast on a horn.

Rails are heavy objects – a 60ft length of 98lb/yd section weighs well over ¾ ton – and putting one into position without mechanical aid called for a good deal of manual strength. A relaying gang would consist of several dozen men.

Every yard of railway track had to be walked and inspected every day of the year, irrespective of weather or any other circumstances. The track was divided into 'lengths', and each length had its gang. They were equipped with a modicum of tools and a small four-wheeled truck, usually hand propelled, to move the heavier items from their trackside cabins to the scene of operations. These trucks, or bogies, were quite

On a certain preserved steam railway, a volunteer guard was heard to remark that he wouldn't mind a job with the permanent way gang. 'Whenever I go past them,' he said, 'they're simply leaning on their shovels and watching the train!'

Fig. 149. A motorised permanent way trolley at Binegar, Somerset & Dorset Joint Railway. In this photograph, taken in July 1953, the ever-helpful permanent way gang are giving a lift to a traveller who has missed his train! (*Ivo Peters*)

light, and easily lifted off their pressed-steel wheels, so that the whole thing could be quickly removed from the track if a train approached. Nevertheless, the signalman was informed and the bogie was given absolute possession of a track section as if it were a train.

By the 1950s, the cost of labour had overtaken that of machinery, and tracklaying machines were available. The method of operation was to propel the wagon, with its jibs extended sideways, to a wagon loaded with pre-assembled 60ft lengths of track. A length was lifted, then the wagon was moved to the end of the track. The length was lowered into position, and the rail ends secured. The wagon loaded with lengths was then pushed onto the newly installed track, and the procedure repeated. The track panel would be manoeuvred into the correct position manually while it was still suspended. Once it was down, the train moved forward and the next length of track went down. The rail joints were effected, ballast tamped and compacted under the sleepers, and adjustments made by raising the entire track using jacks. Such work would be done at night, and there was no time to lose: trains might well be running over it from about 6.00 a.m. In the south of England, the work went ahead regardless of the weather; in Yorkshire gangs did not work in the rain!

When walking his length, the ganger's main tools were a long-handled spanner for adjusting rail joints, and a sledgehammer for replacing keys that worked loose: the phenomenon of rail creep, discussed above, meant that he soon learned where the rail could be

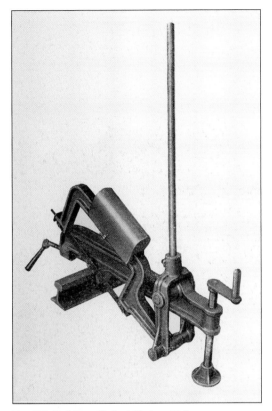

Fig. 150. Rail Saw. (*Robert Hudson Ltd*)

Fig. 151. Rail drilling machine. (*Robert Hudson Ltd*)

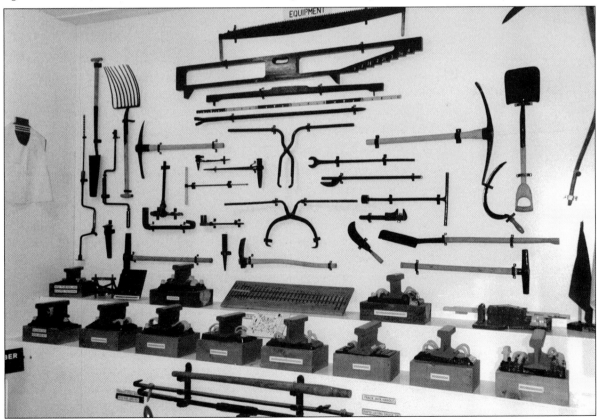

Fig. 152. A selection of platelayers' tools displayed at Beverley Military Museum. The augurs on the left are for drilling holes in sleepers, and the fork is for moving ballast. The tongs in the middle are for lifting rails. Just below the saw at the top is a gauge for measuring the distances between rails and tracks. Notice also the collection of different sizes of rails in the foreground. (*John Moore*)

Fig. 153. Inside Midhurst Tunnel, Sussex. The wooden object lying against the left-hand wall is a clearance gauge. It is used to ensure that the track has not moved out of alignment and thus became too close to one side of the tunnel. (*Author*)

expected to work forwards, and where it would work backwards, and the direction he drove the keys would reflect this. Ballast was moved by shovels and forks, the latter rather like gardening forks but broader and with closer-spaced tines. Rail joints were slackened or tightened with a long-handled spanner. Chair bolts were removed and replaced with a box spanner with a T-handle. Spikes were driven with hammer with a specially-shaped head.

More difficult tasks called for specialist equipment. In the days before abrasive wheels powered by a portable internal combustion engine, rails were cut using a portable hacksaw tool which was clamped to the rail and operated by pushing a long lever back and forth, see Fig. 150. Holes for fishplates were drilled by hand ratchet drills, or by rather faster two-man drills, see Fig. 151. Rails were bent or curved by judicious use of a cramp, commonly known as a 'Jim Crow' – goodness knows why.

Your author would like to direct the reader's attention to Fig. 146 in the previous chapter. As a young enthusiast, aged about eighteen or nineteen, he cut the rails for the straight track attached to the turnout with an ordinary hacksaw. Each cut took about twenty minutes and was very good wrist and elbow exercise!

Fig. 154. A rail-bending cramp, commonly known as a 'Jim Crow'. The two ends at the bottom of the photograph are hooked round the bottom edge of the rail, and the central screw is then tightened with a tommy bar until the rail assumes the desired curve or bend. (*Author*)

Even the methods used to get the men to the scene of work improved in more recent years. Formerly they were expected to walk, or they might be given a lift by a friendly goods train crew. Motorised trolleys were popularised by D. Wickham & Co. Ltd, of Ware, Hertfordshire, and have made a great difference. Other varieties of transport include pump trolleys, operated by two men, and varieties of rail cycles, some of which were home-made and were basically a bicycle with an outrigger.

Once organised in small local gangs, permanent way staff are now formed into larger gangs based at central depots. They are transported, with their equipment, by road to the scene of operations, which may be 25 miles or more away. They are now provided with proper washing and toilet facilities. The old lineside cabins have been replaced by mess facilities in the road vehicles.

The railway companies developed fleets of specialised wagons for track maintenance, and British Railways continued in the same vein. Most

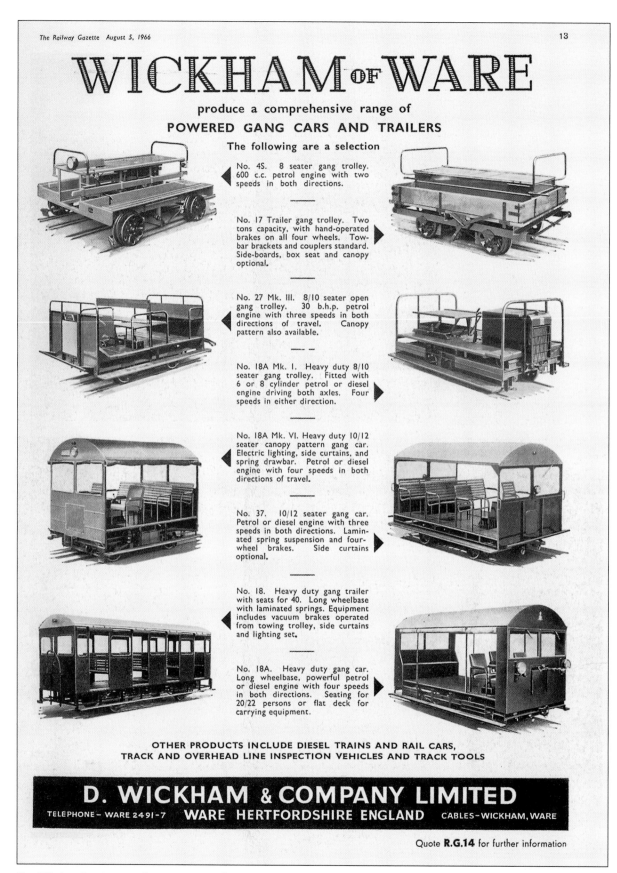

Fig. 155. An advertisement showing a range of permanent way and inspection trolleys produced by D. Wickham & Co. Ltd. (*Railway Gazette, 5 August 1966*)

Fig. 156. A Wickham railcar on the Longmoor Military Railway, 1955. (*Author*)

Fig. 157. A Great Western 10 ton ballast wagon of 1913. The side doors drop down and the ballast is shovelled manually onto the trackside. This was typical of hundreds of wagons built for many railways. This particular specimen, preserved at the National Railway Museum, is of all-iron construction and shows that the floors of such wagons were prone to rust, an inherent weakness. (*Author*)

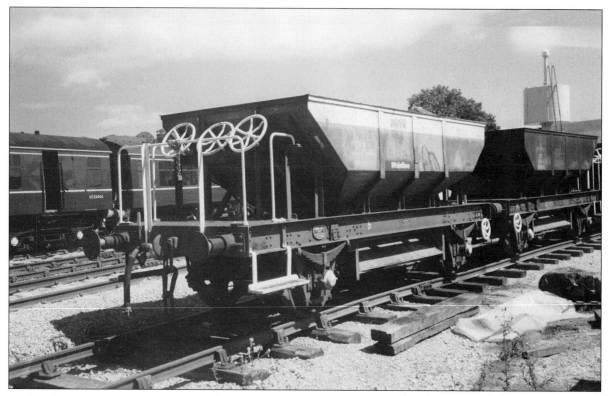

Fig. 158. All-steel hopper ballast wagon. Note the end platform, with step and handrails for easy access from rail level, and controls enabling the ballast to be deposited to left, right, and/or in the centre of the track. (*Author*)

Fig. 159. In the 1930s the Southern Railway introduced some really splendid bogie hopper wagons for ballast from Meldon Quarry, on Dartmoor. Their capacity was 40 tons and tare weight 20 tons 10 cwt. The design was taken up by British Railways, and many BR-built examples are still to be seen, identical in all but details – for example, different bogies or air brakes instead of vacuum. (*H.C. Casserley*)

prominent were ballast wagons. They ranged from open wagons of about 6 tons capacity with drop sides, from which ballast could be shovelled manually onto the trackside to be spread, again manually, amongst the sleepers, to sophisticated hopper wagons with air-operated doors, from which the flow of ballast could be accurately controlled onto the track. Bringing up the rear was a special brake van, which had the added function of a plough-shaped device to spread the ballast more evenly across the track and thus ease the work of the track gangs.

Fig. 160. A London Midland & Scottish Railway-designed 16 ton plough brake van. The short wheelbase enables the twin ploughs, seen here in the raised position, to be mounted at the vehicle ends where they can be controlled and their action observed. The brake wheel is inside the van body. The bar across the doorways is the only protection the crew has against falling off the verandas when the van is in motion. (*Author*)

The 40 ton bogie ballast wagons first introduced in the 1930s by the Southern Railway are illustrated at Fig. 159. A second batch was built in 1937. The first wagons had diamond-frame bogies, as shown in the illustration, but the later examples had cast-steel bogies similar to an American design. Further examples, with a plate-frame bogie, were built by British Railways. In the late 1960s a 'stretched' version was constructed, which took 50 tons of ballast. The design was not completely satisfactory, and in 1968 the wagons were all strengthened at Crewe Works. Further construction reverted to 40 tons capacity, twenty-five being built at Shildon in 1970, with an extra three in 1971 to replace accident casualties. Shildon produced a further 100 in 1971, fitted with both air and vacuum brakes. In appearance they were very similar to the excellent Southern Railway design of the 1930s, on which it has been very hard to improve.

A variety of wagons were built for carrying sleepers, and a typical example is shown in Fig. 163. The flat wagon has a lowered floor and its buffer beams are raised at the ends. It is fitted with two cranes to assist with the unloading of rails and sleepers, and even entire lengths, or

Fig. 161. A view of the 'ship's steering wheel' on the end platform of the ballast brake van shown in Fig. 160. It was used to raise and lower the plough in front of the wheels. (*Author*)

Fig. 162. Ballast trains are heavy. This one, near Midsomer Norton on the Somerset & Dorset Joint Railway, is hauled by a 7F class 2–8–0 No. 53800 and banked up the 1 in 50 by 4F class 0–6–0 No. 44096 on a Sunday in January 1958. (*Ivo Peters*)

Fig. 163. A flat wagon fitted with two cranes for unloading sleepers and/or rails. (*Author*)

panels, of track. As mentioned above, these wagons first became available in the 1940s, and proved a great boon, carrying out in a few hours work that had previously taken days – and using far less labour.

Probably the most dramatic piece of civil engineering equipment is the so-called breakdown crane. Since this is occasionally called upon to lift a locomotive, a capacity of 45 tons or more is not uncommon. But such

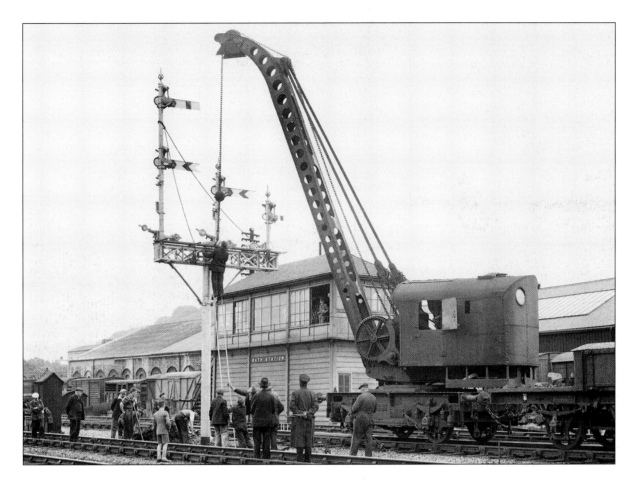

cranes are usually deployed to carry out far more mundane tasks, such as positioning signals, signal gantries, footbridges and overhead electrical equipment, for example. When they are turned to an angle, such cranes become inherently unstable and as a result they are equipped with extending transverse beams and jacks, so that the load can be spread and the risk of the crane capsizing minimised. But accidents can and do happen. The cranes can move under their own power, albeit at little more than walking pace. They were originally steam powered, but diesel and diesel-electric cranes appeared later, which can be switched on and started virtually at the touch of a button; steam cranes had to be kept in steam constantly so that they were instantly available in the event of an emergency.

Development of mechanised track maintenance equipment has been rapid, principally in Switzerland and Austria. Ballast cleaning equipment, relaying machines, track lifting and realigning machines have all made their appearance, in some cases only to be quickly supplanted by even more effective and sophisticated equipment. In recent years, track relaying geometry has been improved by ballast-handling plant with laser control, enabling curves and junctions to be positioned so that they may be negotiated at maximum speeds.

Fig. 164. A typical use for a railway crane. Here a new upper-quadrant signal is being installed at Bath, Somerset & Dorset Joint Railway. This job was done on a Sunday morning in 1956, when there were be few trains about. (*Ivo Peters*)

A MISCELLANY

Bad weather always presents problems, and clearing points of snow and ice has exercised railways since their inception. Compacted snow collects in turnouts between stock rails and switch rails, and between running rails and check rails. Traditionally, labour has been employed to dig it out and, after it has reformed, to dig it out again. But labour has become expensive, and other methods have been explored.

Most promising are electric heaters, but a supply of electricity is not always easy to arrange, especially at a remote junction. Machines blowing hot air have been tried, initially with promising results, but they need labour to operate them and so the expense of manpower is not avoided. Just after the Second World War, the idea was tried of mounting an aircraft jet engine on a wagon so that its hot exhaust gases would thaw frozen points. Quite apart from the problem of restraining the wagon from trying to become airborne, it was found that although the jet did indeed thaw the packed snow, unfortunately it then re-froze into solid ice, and was harder to shift than ever! Chemical products, aimed at preventing the snow from settling and usually based on salt, have been tried with indifferent results. The best method seems to be the cheapest if not the easiest: the signalman must operate the points at frequent intervals, simply to dislodge snow and prevent it building up. After that, manpower, with picks and shovels, remains the answer.

In Britain there is only one avalanche shelter of the kind that is quite common elsewhere, for example, in Switzerland. This is at Cruach Cutting, north of Rannoch, and has been converted into an artificial tunnel some 200 yards long. (There is an avalanche shelter at Y Friog, near Barmouth, but this guards against rockfalls rather than snow.) However, a form of snow-blower is occasionally employed on exposed stretches in Scotland, and an example is illustrated in Fig. 165. This is like a wooden fence, made of boards, and is set with one edge close to the ground while the other is 8–10ft high. It is designed to funnel the prevailing wind in such a way as to blow the snow clear of the track. Five examples have been used at various times in Scotland and have proved quite effective.

Further devices, often seen in northern England, are snow fences. These are wooden fences, parallel to and several yards away from the usual railway fence. Snow piles up against them, and is thus prevented from drifting onto the railway. The devices are effective but, like the snow-

Fig. 165. Snow-blower near Forsinard, on the Inverness–Wick line, looking south. (*H.C. Casserley*)

Fig. 166. Snow fences between Barrhill and Glenwhilly, Scotland. (*H.C. Casserley*)

blowers, can be overwhelmed by the fiercest winters. Cuttings are particularly vulnerable.

The rotary snowplough, of a type quite common in North America and continental Europe, has never found favour in Britain. Instead, railways have relied on wedge-shaped ploughs. These have been specially built, and in recent years were converted from redundant steam locomotive tenders. The usual procedure is to couple two locomotives back to back, with a snow plough at each end, and then to patrol the line constantly to prevent any build-up of snow. But in the last resort, labour has to be used to shovel the snow out, or the line has to be closed until the thaw. David L. Smith* tells of blizzards at the Chirmorie Summit, near Barrhill, Ayrshire, on the Glasgow & South Western Railway, in the winter of 1908–9, and of the railway's efforts to clear them. In the severe winter of 1946–7, cuttings on the Settle and Carlisle line were cleared by German prisoners of war.

* David L. Smith, *The Stranraer Road*, in C.J. Allen (ed.), Trains Annual 1950 (Ian Allan Ltd).

Fig. 167. Dalnaspidal station,
Highland Railway, facing south,
c. 1930. Note the signal wires,
carried on posts to the right of
the tracks. (*H.C. Casserley*)

Yet another precaution against snow is illustrated in Fig. 167. The
Highland Railway carried signal wires on high posts, clear of snow. The
height of the posts gives an idea of what winter could bring in those
exposed and remote areas.

FLANGE GREASERS

On sharp curves, the flanges of the wheels press against the outer rail. To
ease their progress, flange greasers are sometimes employed. There are
several types, made by various manufacturers, and a Mills Hurcol

Fig. 168. A flange greaser, laid
outside the track. Similar
appliances can be laid inside the
track, i.e. between the running
rails, if necessary. (*Author*)

example is illustrated in Fig. 168. Although this greaser is placed outside the rails, it is operated by the treadle which places the grease on the inside of the rail. Whilst it is desirable to grease the flanges traversing the curve, the tyres of locomotives or motor coaches should not be greased, for obvious reasons.

WAGON RETARDERS

Hardly ever seen by the travelling public, but nevertheless part of railway trackwork, were wagon retarders in hump marshalling yards. It should be explained that in the days of single-wagon freight consignments from one end of the country to the other, wagons were sorted and re-sorted at fairly frequent intervals. Given the amount of time they spent standing in marshalling yards, and the low speeds of the typical steam-hauled freight train, Dr Richard Beeching calculated that the average wagon speed from starting point to destination was approximately 0.5mph! Of course, this made the railways sitting targets for competition from road haulage, which offers a door-to-door service that the railways can never hope to match. So the railways concentrated on bulk goods that could be moved by the trainload and which did not need remarshalling *en route* – the hump marshalling yard faded into history.

Gravity was used to aid shunting and sorting wagons. If the wagons were pushed up a short but steep hill, termed a 'hump', once over the top they would roll by gravity into a fan of sidings. Smart work on the ground, or in an adjacent control tower, could change the points and direct each wagon into the correct siding for onward transmission. But if the sidings were full, the wagons might run down at increasing speed and collide with some force, damaging the wagon, or the goods inside it, or both. The usual method was for men to run alongside each wagon, applying its brake lever. But the risk of slipping or tripping, and falling under the wheels was very great and there were accidents. A form of braking was required and, necessity being the mother of invention, various manufacturers produced 'retarders'. The basic idea was that a steel bar pressed on the inside of the flanges of the wagon wheels, and so slowed its progress.

A further development, from the Dowty Company, was a kind of retarder in reverse: instead of retarding wagons, it could move forward the vehicles that had stopped short. But, in spite of being demonstrated by the manufacturer and actively promoted in the railway technical press, it never went into active service.

WATER SUPPLY

Steam locomotives consume prodigious amounts of water and provision for taking on supplies could once be seen at many stations, as well as at locomotive depots. Under pressure to speed up the mail trains, and the Irish Mail in particular, John Ramsbottom, Locomotive Superintendent of

Fig. 169. GWR 4–6–0 No. 6028 *King George VI* taking water from Sodbury Troughs as she approaches Sodbury Tunnel with the up 'Red Dragon', *c.* 1960. The bridge over the line is an aqueduct and carries a stream. This was necessitated by the cutting, which was excavated through the stream's natural course. (*Ivo Peters*)

the London & North Western Railway, devised a way of replenishing a locomotive's tender without stopping. On a suitable level stretch of track, a long trough was laid down between the rails, and filled with water. The locomotive tender was fitted with a scoop, which could be lowered into the water by the fireman. The speed of the train would force the water up the scoop and into the tender tank. The first set of troughs was installed at Aber, North Wales, in 1860. The idea was brilliantly successful, and troughs were subsequently laid down in many locations. Only the Southern Railway and its constituents never used them, although serious thought was given to installing the systems. The idea spread overseas: the Western Railway of France and the Pennsylvania Railroad of the USA also used track troughs.

The Southern Railway never used track troughs because only the West of England main line from London to Exeter could have benefited from them. But, following a very serious accident in 1904, all trains were required to stop at Salisbury. Locomotives could then either be watered, or even changed completely. The runs from Waterloo to Salisbury and Salisbury to Exeter could each be completed with a single tender full of water.

Some railways habitually used tank locomotives on quite fast trains, and these could be fitted with water pick-up gear which could be operated when the locomotive was running in either direction. Tender locomotives could only pick up when running chimney first. But back to water troughs.

On the LMS, the track was heavily timbered around the sleepers to counteract the effect of heavy splashing which tended to wash the ballast away. Splashing was countered to some extent by the use of plates under the tender, which guided the water towards the scoop. The trough was about 18in wide, with a depth of water of 5in. The top edge was turned inwards to form a lip in an attempt to reduce spillage. The mild steel sections were in lengths of about 14ft. In order to contain the water, the troughs were arranged to rise at each end, and the rails dipped slightly to lower the tender scoop into the water.

The maintenance of water troughs was surprisingly labour-intensive. Quite apart from the need to man an associated water-softening plant by the lineside and the removal of the sludge that it generated, the heavy spray from the use of the troughs made drainage a problem. Furthermore, the troughs themselves tended to collect silt and other debris, and needed to be cleaned out from time to time.

At one time the Great Western Railway had a 4–6–2 locomotive, No. 111 *The Great Bear*. A unique engine for the GWR, it had an eight-wheeled bogie tender. On this tender, the pipe leading upwards from the water scoop ended just below the filler cap, which also did duty as the deflector dome, which was a separate fitting on most other tenders. The story goes that on one occasion this filler cap was not properly secured. All went well until the first track trough was reached. The scoop was lowered, and the torrent of water rushed up the pipe, forced the filler cap open, cascaded over the top of the tender, and hit the end corridor connection of the leading coach with sufficient force to smash it open. A tidal wave then rushed down the corridor, and flooded the coach. The Great Western authorities were said to have gone to great lengths to hush up the incident, which incidentally cost them quite a lot in compensation for ruined luggage, etc.

SIGNALLING

Although this book aims to avoid discussion of signalling, the presence on the track of equipment connected with it perhaps merits a mention. In particular, the Great Western Railway developed a sophisticated system termed Automatic Train Control. First installed in 1906, it was designed to give the driver an indication of the setting of distant signals when visibility could be affected, such as at night, or in conditions of fog or falling snow. Between the rails, just in front of each distant signal, was a ramp with a rail on the upper edge. Below the locomotive was a shoe or plunger which would make contact with the ramp and be lifted as the

Fig. 170. No. 6001 *King Edward VII* on controlled road tests, being turned on the triangle at Filton Junction, 1955. On the left-hand track, the Automatic Train Control ramp is clearly visible. It relates to the signal in the distance. (*Ivo Peters*)

locomotive passed over it. If the signal were at clear, the ramp would be electrified and a bell would sound in the cab. But if the signal were at danger, the ramp would be electrically dead, a siren would sound in the cab, and the brakes would be automatically applied. The driver could cancel the signal and release the brakes. The system failed to safety, that is, if the current was interrupted a 'danger' signal would be given. Also, the driver received a positive indication that the signal was clear.

The 'train control' was demonstrated at a series of trials held in March 1938. A special train, made up to ten coaches weighing 300 tons and headed by the new No. 5055 *Earl of Eldon*, was deliberately run through a distant signal at danger, with the engine crew instructed to continue driving at full speed and to ignore the siren. The train passed the signal at 69mph, and with full steam still applied it came to a dead stand in 900 yards on dead level track. The ramp was 318 yards ahead of the distant signal, which was 1,032 yards ahead of the home signal. The train therefore stopped 450 yards ahead of the danger point. This was a very impressive demonstration.

The Great Western was not the only company to develop such a system. The North Eastern Railway had something similar, which relied on arms below the locomotive striking arms raised or lowered between the rails. Developed by Vincent Raven, later Sir Vincent and Chief Mechanical Engineer of the NER, the system was mechanical, not electric, and suffered from the disadvantage that the impact at speeds of 60mph and above was sometimes sufficient to break the arms off altogether. Furthermore, if the signal were at clear, then no indication was given in the cab, and a driver could not really be sure that he had received the correct message. However, the North Eastern drivers learned to put considerable trust in the system, and drove really fast in adverse weather. For the reasons given (and for reasons of economy) the NER's successor, the London & North Eastern Railway, removed the system from locomotives as they passed through shops and from the track as renewals became due.

The Great Central Railway installed a system called 'Reliostop'. Jointly developed by A.F. Bound, the Signal Superintendent, and W. Rowland, the Chief Draughtsman of the Locomotive Department under J.G. Robinson, this also worked on an arrangement of rail-mounted levers. It provided a trip lever and also a treadle beneath the locomotive. Operation of the treadle on a fixed ramp by the trackside near a distant signal gave a siren warning together with a partial brake application. About halfway between the distant signal and the home, a further warning would be given. Home signals at danger caused a full brake application to be made. But this system was a late developer: by the 1923 Grouping, only twenty locomotives and 40 route miles had been equipped, and the LNER did not take the project further.

The development and installation of all of these systems required a company's signal and telegraph department, operating department, and the locomotive department to cooperate with each other with at least some degree of enthusiasm. The Great Western had the will to promote safety almost regardless of cost, and its system was by far the best. For the others, internal rivalries, an overriding need for financial stringency, or both, saw to it that nothing comparable emerged.

TRAVELLING POST OFFICE

A lineside feature that has disappeared from the main lines and is now only to be found on a couple of preserved lines is the apparatus for exchanging mailbags with trains passing at speed. The General Post Office was not slow to exploit the potential for faster transit of the mail offered by the railways. The Grand Junction Railway carried mail between Birmingham and Warrington from its opening in July 1837, and provided a converted horse box for sorting post *en route* in January 1838. The following January saw the start of the highly dangerous practice of throwing mailbags onto the platforms of stations from passing trains. It will be appreciated that even at speeds as low as 25mph considerable damage could be done, not only to the mail itself but also to anyone who got in the way. A better system was needed. Experiments with apparatus on the mail vans and at the lineside were carried out by a number of engineers. The first trials were conducted at Berkhampstead on 27 October 1838, but the equipment, while working well enough at low speeds, was not able to withstand the rough and tumble of daily use.

Further experiments continued, and by 1848 the apparatus was perfected.

With the exception of the southern lines, the practice spread nationwide. The most famous train was the West Coast Postal from London Euston to Scotland. This was celebrated in the lines of W.H. Auden's well-known poem 'This is the Night Mail crossing the Border, Bringing the cheque and the postal order'. The Travelling Post Office trains still operate, using dedicated electric and diesel-electric powered train sets.

For a variety of reasons, use of the exchange apparatus declined after the Second World War. The higher speeds and faster acceleration of modern diesel and electric motive power made it possible to stop the train to load and unload mails at stations and still maintain overall speeds, and maximum speeds, nudging 125mph, meant that the impact of the mailbags, in their stout leather pouches, was liable to inflict damage on the apparatus and on the mail vans themselves.

Apparatus for picking up the mail consisted of a lineside standard of hanging stout leather pouch or pouches containing the mailbags which could be picked up by a net extended from the side of the train. Setting down the mail required the reverse arrangement: the pouch or pouches were slung from traductor arms on the side of the mail vans, and a stout rope net on the ground caught them as the train sped by.

It is necessary to write in the past tense about this lineside feature. Its use declined, and the last pick-up and set-down took place at Penrith on 4 October 1971. The GPO offered the equipment to anyone who could use it, and sets were acquired by the (modern) Great Central Railway at Loughborough and the Great Western Society at Didcot. Both of these lines run demonstrations from time to time.

CABLE RAILWAYS

In the very earliest days, the ability of a steam locomotive to grip the rails with sufficient friction to haul a worthwhile load was doubted, so much so that the Liverpool & Manchester Railway, contemplating cable haulage, organised the famous Rainhill Trials to see if a locomotive could do what was required. As is well known, George and Robert Stephenson's *Rocket* won the competition, and there was no more talk of cable haulage on the Liverpool & Manchester.

However, the idea remained attractive. With the winding engine in a stationary position, it could be made as large as required with no weight or other constraints, and did not have to haul its own bulk. Nevertheless, it did have to haul the weight of the cable. The system was used successfully on the London & Blackwall Railway, where a system of slip carriages gave a good service between all stations. It was also deployed on steep inclines. The inclines from London Euston to Camden and from Glasgow Queen Street to Cowlairs were later converted to locomotive haulage, but those on the Cromford & High Peak Railway in Derbyshire remained cable-operated until the line closed on 21 April 1967. The

Fig.171. This view, looking up a cliff railway at Lynmouth, shows the type of rollers used to guide the cable. Notice that the two tracks are set very close together: they only separate where the cars actually pass. (*Author*)

Fig. 172. The bottom of Sheep Pasture Incline, Cromford & High Peak Railway, showing the way in which the cable is supported. The tracks diverge either side of a safety pit for runaways. It will be noted that the left-hand track is marginally higher than the one on the right. (*H.C. Casserley*)

Cromford & High Peak was a freight-only line (officially, at any rate). The Bowes Railway, in County Durham, was and remains a mineral railway. Now preserved, it is the last cable-operated railway in the country and is well worth a visit to see a unique method of operation.

The track for such lines was much the same as normal, i.e. bull-head rail in chairs on wooden sleepers. A roller to carry the cable was mounted in the centre of the track. On curves the roller gave way to pulleys, which might be inclined as required. Inclines were usually operated by a winding engine at the summit, though occasionally the funicular, or counter-balance method, was chosen. The slate quarry inclines of North Wales were prime examples of the second method. Here, the wagons going down pulled those ascending; it was, of course, necessary for the load to be with the gradient, so that the descending wagons were loaded and the ascending ones were empty. On such lines, because the two trains can only pass in the middle, the tracks can be laid very close together, as in Fig. 171, or only three rails can be installed, with the centre rail being common to ascending and descending trains. On the three-rail system, the two tracks must be separated in the middle of the incline to allow the vehicles to pass. Overseas, the cable railway and the funicular have been developed into a system of some sophistication, and this received extended treatment in Chapter 3.

TWELVE

ACCIDENTS

The purpose of this chapter is not to persuade the reader that purchasing a railway ticket involves taking one's life into one's hands. Rather it is intended to discuss mishaps that have been directly attributable to a failure of either the permanent way or a civil engineering feature. Collisions that have taken place in tunnels owing to signalling failure or mismanagement are not included, horrific though the consequences have occasionally been.

The first Tay Bridge failure was by far the worst incident of its kind. The bridge collapsed during a storm on 28 December 1879 with the loss of about seventy-five lives. The story has been told in great detail elsewhere, and those seeking more information are referred to the bibliography. To summarise, the design, by Thomas Bouch, took no account of the pressure of the wind. The contractors, Hopkins, Gilkes & Co., were guilty of extremely poor workmanship – for example, the cast-iron columns of the bridge, which were cast at a temporary foundry set up at Wormit on the banks of the Tay estuary opposite Dundee, contained numerous blow-holes. The on-site foreman had them filled with a compound called 'Beaumont's Egg', which took paint in the same way as metal and so disguised the faults. After the bridge was opened, Queen Victoria travelled across it on her way to Balmoral and knighted Thomas Bouch. But when it fell, during a ferocious gale, it took an entire train with it, from which there were no survivors. The locomotive was recovered, repaired and returned to work. The fallen spans were retrieved, with the remains of the coaches still inside them. A new bridge was built alongside the remains of the first and is of much sturdier design and construction, although it re-used many of the girders of the original. The first bridge was for single track only; the second was for double. It continues to stand securely.

There was a Victorian vogue for casting bridge girders in iron. The bridges in question spanned a road or a stream, not much wider than 30ft or so, but the Railway Inspectorate of the Board of Trade was uneasy about the trend. Cast iron is strong in compression, but brittle in tension, and we have already seen that it was unsuitable for rails. It was inevitable that, sooner or later, a cast-iron bridge would fail, and disaster struck early in 1847, only six months after the opening of the Shrewsbury and Chester Railway. To gain access to Chester, the line joined the Chester & Holyhead Railway at Saltney Junction, and then crossed the River Dee by Robert Stephenson's cast-iron bridge. This structure consisted of three 98ft spans of cast-iron girders resting on stone piers. The third span of the bridge collapsed under the 6.15 p.m. train from Chester to Ruabon. The locomotive just managed to clear the girders as they collapsed, but the tender and the rest of the train fell with them. Five people died and sixteen were injured, which was perhaps a fairly light level of casualties considering the whole of the train, apart from the locomotive, ended up in the river. In his report, the Inspector-General of Railways, Captain Simmons, condemned the bridge girders as too weak. He further castigated the whole principle of construction as unsound. This report brought the use of cast-iron bridges seriously into question.

There have been several cases of bridges being washed away by floods. The earliest was probably on 20 January 1846 when the South Eastern Railway's timber trestle bridge over a backwater of the River Medway between Penshurst and Tonbridge was carried away by flood waters following heavy rain. A goods train came to grief and the driver was the only casualty.

More serious was the mishap that befell the Highland Railway in June 1914. Torrential rain in the Grampians of Scotland caused a road bridge to collapse. The debris acted as a dam, penning back the water until it broke through. The resulting tidal wave damaged Carr Bridge on the Highland Railway, and the 10.00 a.m. Glasgow–Inverness train ran onto the bridge. The locomotive's tender and the first two coaches were derailed. The driver stopped the train with the two derailed coaches on the far side of the bridge, the next three coaches on the bridge, and the remainder south of it. The driver walked back to tell the guard of the situation, and the bridge gave way completely. The fourth coach fell into the torrent, and five passengers died.

There have been several accidents due to landslides and rock falls in exposed areas. The Caledonian Railway installed wires along the side of the Callendar to Oban route which, if broken or distorted by rock falls, would automatically return signals to danger. But there was no such protection in February 1880 for a freight train from Monmouth to Chepstow. It hit a large rock which had fallen from the foundations of an old tramroad above. Damage was quite extensive – the locomotive turned upside down and the driver was pinned under it. Fortunately, he was rescued uninjured.

At Y Friog, above Barmouth, the railway follows a ledge in the cliff side, with the main coast road above at the top of the cliff. A rockfall occurred on the evening of 1 January 1883 and a Machynlleth to Barmouth train ran into it. The locomotive, Cambrian Railways No. 29 *Pegasus*, mounted the obstruction and went over the cliff, killing the driver and fireman. The same thing happened again early on 4 March 1933, and the morning mail train, hauled by Great Western Railway No. 874 (formerly Cambrian No. 54) ran into the debris. This engine also went over the cliff, and the crew were killed. The line is now protected by a Swiss-style avalanche shelter.

There have been several other examples of trains running into landslides, both in cuttings and elsewhere. A very early incident took place on Christmas Eve 1841 on the Great Western Railway. The 4.30 a.m. goods train from Paddington to Bristol consisted of the 2–4–0 locomotive *Hecla*, one six-wheeled third-class coach, one four-wheeled third-class coach, a covered van and seventeen goods wagons. Abnormally heavy rain had caused the side of Sonning Cutting to slip, and the train ran into the obstruction. Eight passengers were killed and seventeen were injured. The Inspecting Officer, Sir Frederic Smith, wrote in his report: 'I do not imagine that any engineer would have thought it necessary to give the sides of this cutting a greater slope than two to one, and therefore there has been, in my opinion, no error in the construction.' Although the Great Western escaped censure for its civil engineering, it came in for heavy criticism for its treatment of the unfortunate third-class passengers. The coach sides were only 2ft high; above this they were open to the elements. The seats were wooden planks just 18in wide, and the buffers were unsprung. Also, the practice of including passenger coaches in what was nominally a goods train was strongly condemned: protection in the event of an accident was minimal. Only three years later Gladstone's Railway Regulation Act was passed, compelling all railways to operate at least one train for third-class passengers who were to be carried in weatherproof carriages at a fare of not more than one penny per mile. They were to stop at all stations, and were to run at a speed of not less than 12mph, inclusive of stops. It is true that some railways honoured the Act somewhat grudgingly, running the 'Parliamentary' in the middle of the night, but it spelled the end of the open 'coach'.

Track which has been under repair by permanent way men has been the cause of more than one mishap. A well-known example occurred in 1865. The South Eastern Railway's Beult viaduct, near Staplehurst, which carried the tracks just 10ft above a muddy stream, was undergoing renewal work on the longitudinal beams that carried the rails on the tops of the cast-iron girders. The permanent way gang had replaced thirty-one of the thirty-two baulks, and the foreman, John Benge, intended to finish the job between the passage of an up train at 2.51 p.m. and one in the opposite direction at 4.15 p.m. It seems that familiarity bred contempt: there was inadequate protection of the work, although detonators were supposed to be placed on the tracks up to 1,000 yards away in each direction to give warning. Mr Benge's copy of the timetable made reference to the Folkestone Boat Express. This train's times were dependent on the arrival of the steamer from France, which in turn was dependent on the tides. Hence the time of its arrival could vary at the place where the work was being carried out, and it seems that Benge misread the timetable, or misunderstood what he read. The 'tidal' was due to pass Headcorn at 3.15; Benge was expecting it at 5.20.

With the new baulk in place, but two lengths of rail still out of their chairs, the express approached the scene at speed. The destruction was thorough, with ten passengers killed and forty-nine injured. Novelist Charles Dickens was among the passengers; he was in the leading coach, which was undamaged. Dickens was unharmed and gave assistance to the injured. He had been working on the manuscript of *Our Mutual Friend* in the train. He was quite severely traumatised and probably never fully recovered from the accident. He died on 9 June 1870, the fifth anniversary of the accident.

A permanent way gang at Raynes Park, Southern Railway, on 25 May 1933 had been lifting and packing ballast under sleepers. The track might have withstood a train moving at slow speed, but no warnings had been given and all five coaches of the 3.10 p.m. from Waterloo to Alton were derailed. A Southampton to Waterloo train then collided with the derailed coaches. Five passengers were killed and thirty-four were injured. The driver of the Southampton train was also seriously hurt.

The Southern was not very lucky with its track, and one cause of problems was the use of shingle from the beach at Eastbourne as ballast. The drawbacks associated with the use of shingle have been discussed in Chapter 7 above. In the case of the Sevenoaks accident on 24 August 1927, another contributory factor was surging water in the side tanks of the locomotive. The locomotive, No. A800 *River Cray*, was one of the 'River' class 2–6–4 tank engines. There had been complaints from enginemen that these locomotives rolled at speed. The engine derailed on the downhill gradient from Polhill Tunnel to Sevenoaks. The locomotive then burst a set of trailing catch points, and the rest of the train left the rails. The train now approached Shoreham Lane Bridge, where each track went beneath a single arch with a retaining wall on the left and a bridge pier on the right. Although derailed, the locomotive and the first two coaches passed through the bridge, suffering a good deal of damage in the process. But the next coach ended up broadside against the bridge piers, and it was here that most of the serious casualties occurred. The following coach, the Pullman car *Carmen*, withstood the impact magnificently. The last two coaches were the only ones to sustain no serious damage.

At the subsequent internal inquiry, the engineer, R.E.L. Maunsell, insisted that the locomotives were perfectly stable on good track, and tests on the LNER main line bore him out. The Civil Engineer, George Ellson, insisted that his track was in good order, but it was shown that a cloudburst earlier in the day had undermined the foundations at the scene of the accident. The General Manager, Sir Herbert Walker, concluded that locomotives which were only safe on perfect track, were a distinct liability. He gave orders that 'River' class locomotives were to be immediately withdrawn and converted into tender engines. He also instructed that the whole of the main line from London to Dover was to be reballasted with granite chippings. The accident was very severe: thirteen passengers lost their lives and twenty sustained serious injury. A further seventy-one later wrote to the railway complaining of minor injuries.

A most unusual track fault occurred at Burntisland, Fife, and was responsible for the derailment of a coal train on 8 July 1998. Screws put into four sleepers were defective, and over a sixty-year period had worked loose. Railtrack, by then the authority responsible for the permanent way, reported that the four sleepers were the only ones found to be defective in a search throughout the network.

Fig. 173. The scene at Shoreham Lane Bridge, 24 August 1927. (*LCGB/ Ken Nunn Collection*)

It is not often that a viaduct collapses, but such incidents have happened. One, on the Great Western, was touched upon in Chapter 7. The Lancashire & Yorkshire Railway's line from Huddersfield to Penistone experienced two such mishaps. A timber viaduct at Mytholmbridge was nearly finished when, on 19 February 1849, a strong gale developed and three-quarters of it collapsed, fortunately without injury to the labour force. It was completed as a timber viaduct, but the railway company realised that it would eventually need replacing with masonry. Work on the replacement started in July 1864, but progress was slow. The new viaduct consisted of thirteen arches. Completion was not far off when cracks were noticed in the seventh pier from the Huddersfield end. As a remedial measure, three buttresses were added, but on 3 December 1865 the entire viaduct collapsed. An eye witness reported that the arches fell one after another, like a stack of dominoes. The cause was soon discovered: the foundation of pier seven had been built half on rock and half on gravel, which had made it unstable. In spite of a suggestion that the viaduct be replaced with an embankment, it was rebuilt, eventually opening to traffic on 11 March 1867.

A rather more dramatic incident on the same line was the collapse of two arches of Penistone viaduct on 2 February 1916. Heavy rains had swollen the River Don, which the viaduct crossed, and the foundations of the offending pier had been scoured as a result. The arches fell, leaving the rails suspended across the abyss – and a locomotive on the rails. The crew felt the arch giving way under the locomotive, and reached safety just before the arches fell. The locomotive, 2–4–2T No. 661, hung for a long second on the rails, then turned and fell into the valley 85ft below. Recovery of the engine was extraordinarily difficult. Out of reach of cranes, it was eventually cut into manageable pieces and dragged up to the rails piecemeal. Once the debris had been returned to Horwich Works, the usable pieces were incorporated into a new No. 661. The viaduct was rebuilt, and traffic resumed on 14 August 1916. Occurring as it did at the height of the First World War, the accident was not reported much beyond the local press, and even now references to it are sparse.

A case of a broken rail end resulted in a derailment of a Southern electric train as it approached Sturt Lane Junction (see Fig. 138, Chapter 8). The track in question consisted of 45ft rails of 95lb/yard weight laid in 1930 and re-sleepered in 1948. The rails had worn to about 86lb, 2lb above the permissible minimum. The accident happened on 22 November 1956, when the leading bogie of an eight-coach train travelling at moderate speed became derailed as it passed over a broken rail end. The train was quickly brought to a standstill, but was slightly foul of the adjoining down through track. The guard acted promptly and signalled an approaching steam-hauled express to stop. The driver of the express caught sight of the signal and applied his brakes, but was unable to avoid grazing the electric train. There were no casualties, but the delay to traffic was substantial.

In a distressing accident at Hatfield on 17 October 2000 a Kings Cross–Leeds express was derailed at 115mph, resulting in the death of four people and injuries to over thirty others. There is a suggestion that a broken rail may have been responsible, and several stretches of the network were closed by Railtrack in the aftermath for a thorough examination. It is too soon to comment further.

Nevertheless, accidents due to track failures are rare. This is not simply due to chance but is entirely the result of generally excellent standards of initial construction, and maintenance after installation.

THIRTEEN

TRAMWAY TRACK

The street tramway has a long and honourable history. From the first horse-drawn systems to steam-operated lines and finally electrification, they were to be found in most towns and cities of any size. Of these, only Blackpool Corporation, with its route from Squire's Gate to Fleetwood, survives. It has now been joined by the first of the so-called 'super-trams' at Sheffield, Manchester, Croydon and Wolverhampton. Other lines are to follow.

The problems faced by the original rail-borne trams were different to those of the orthodox railway. Curves were much sharper – the tram needed to go round street corners. Gradients were much fiercer, as the number of runaways testifies. The track needed to be flush with the street surface to present the least possible hazard to other road users.

Fig. 174. Grooved tramway rails laid in ballast at the National Tramway Museum at Crich. The lip on the inside of the rails enabled the space between the rails to be filled up to road level. (*Author*)

Fig. 175. This view of track relaying at Briggate Junction, Leeds, in 1899 gives a good idea of the complexity of such installations. (*Tramway and Railway World*)

The tramways developed a number of special rails. First in the field was the spike rail, which was laid on longitudinal sleepers and spiked directly to them through the groove in the rail. Then came a T-section rail, which was secured to cast-iron stools by means of cotter pins. The stools were placed at 3ft intervals and cast in concrete; the surface of the road between the rails was finished off with cobblestones. Finally, a rail very similar to railway practice, but with a lip on the inner edge, became popular. The objective, of course, was to ensure that the road could be brought up to the level of the top of the rail to present as smooth a surface as possible. A problem for other road users, especially cyclists, arose when a tram line drew close to the pavement and had to be crossed at an oblique angle. Many a cyclist came to grief at such places.

Pointwork created a minor problem. The moving points of normal turnouts presented a hazard, so a simpler version was developed with just one moving point. This can be seen in Fig. 179.

The heavy pounding to which tramway points and crossings were subjected made them an obvious application for the cast-steel crossing mentioned in Chapter 7. Crucible steel was used originally, with manganese steel inserts, but from about 1905 the entire crossings were cast in manganese steel.

With rail joints buried under the road surface, maintenance was always a problem. Tram rail joints were originally fished in the normal railway manner, but the bolts soon worked loose. Various patent jointing devices, such as the anchor joint (a piece of rail rivetted to the undersides of the adjoining rail ends) gave satisfaction up to a point, but welded joints were

Fig. 176. A fine example of cast-steel crossings by Edgar Allen & Co., Sheffield, for the track fan for Kirkstall Depot, Leeds. It was 346ft long and 48ft wide, and was one of the largest layouts the firm had ever attempted. (*Tramway and Railway World*)

found to be the real answer. The alumino-thermit process became available around the beginning of the twentieth century. In this process, a mould with a funnel-shaped crucible was clamped around the rail ends. A powder, consisting of a mixture of aluminium and red iron oxide, was mixed with steel chippings, placed in the crucible, and ignited. The aluminium and red iron oxide burned with a heat sufficiently intense to melt the steel, which flowed into the mould around the join, and only needed grinding to produce a perfect joint. The experience on most tramway systems was that such a joint was permanent.

Fig. 177. The end of the road. Buffer stops at Meadowhall on the Sheffield Super Tram system. These buffers are arranged to slide along the rails, and offer some retarding force. If the worst comes to the worst, however, the brick wall at the end of the track looks pretty solid. (*Author*)

Fig. 178. Interlaced track at the National Tramway Museum, Crich. The tram in the distance has been running on the left-hand track. (*Author*)

Fig. 179. Tramway pointwork at the National Tramway Museum at Crich. It will be noted that only the left-hand blade moves; when set for the track diverging to the left, the point blade acts on the backs of the wheel flanges. (*Author*)

Fig. 180. The triangular junction at Pond's Forge, Sheffield. Points to note include the extremely sharp curves, the check rails, the cast-steel crossings, the 'cattle grid' to discourage trespassing, and the signalling sensor between the track on the left-hand curve. (*Author*)

Fig. 181. A tram bound for Malin Bridge passing over the Pond's Forge junction, and showing the sharpness of the curves. Again, the cast-steel crossings, most of which are curved, are worthy of note. (*Author*)

Where there was a need to negotiate narrow streets, and occasionally narrow overbridges, interlaced or gauntletted track was sometimes used. The example shown in Fig. 178 comes from the National Tramway Museum at Crich. It will be seen that, although the rails come together to form almost a single line under the bridge, there are in fact no points as such, and no moving parts. Thus the risk of a tram taking the wrong line was obviated, and maintenance was less expensive, but it still needed precautions against head-on collisions.

It will be apparent that the flanges of trams are less pronounced than those on main line trains, and that the flangeways at points and crossings are less pronounced. This has had a curious effect when it has been necessary to operate railway rolling stock over tramway tracks. In the case of Glasgow, the tram tracks were laid to a gauge of 4ft 7⅜in so that railway wagons hauled by electric locomotives could run on their flanges.

Not all tramway track used grooved rails. In some cases, especially where main line rolling stock needed to pass on a regular basis, ordinary track was used. It was fitted with continuous check rails to both running rails, and the surface was filled in with tarmac or concrete. Such tracks would typically be found in dock areas or in rail-connected factories. A very celebrated example was the tramway from Weymouth Town station to the Harbour. This ran through the streets of Weymouth, and its most spectacular operation was the passage of the Channel Islands Boat Express – nine or ten main-line corridor coaches hauled by an 0–6–0 pannier tank locomotive. Before the tramway was closed, the boat trains were diverted to the Southern route to Waterloo, and were hauled by class 33 diesel-electric locomotives. It need hardly be added that maintenance of track under such conditions was something of a nightmare for those involved.

The re-emergence of the street tramway in this country in recent years has been noted above. The Sheffield system has a most interesting triangular junction at Pond's Forge shown in Fig. 180. This is above the street on a viaduct which is also a pedestrian footway, and so the interested tram-watcher does not need to trespass to see the junction.

Trespassing is actively discouraged, and to this end the system employs 'cattle grids', as can be seen in the photographs. It will be noted that the track consists of flat-bottomed rail, continuously welded, mounted on concrete sleepers on plain track, with timber sleepers at crossings. Pandrol fixings are employed, but the rail nearest the camera in Fig. 181 is supported by chairs. Even though the curves are extremely tight, check rails are only provided opposite crossings. But the single track approach to Meadowhall, which features a sharp curve combined with a pronounced change of gradient, is provided with a check rail.

FOURTEEN

'TRACK OF OLD RAILWAY'

Fig. 182. 'Track of Old
Railway': the West Somerset
Mineral Railway, dismantled by
1918, here seen near Washford
in 1957. (*Author*)

These most evocative words, familiar to all who have pored over older editions of the Ordnance Survey's 1in maps, reveal the existence on the ground of traces of a railway that no longer exists. Reasons for a line's disappearance can be many and varied: duplication by old companies may have led to rationalisation in the Grouping era, as happened in the Ramsgate area in the late 1920s and early '30s; a mine may have become exhausted or uneconomic to continue, cutting off the railway's staple traffic, as at the West Somerset Mineral Railway; or there may have been a landslide, such as blocked the Callendar and Oban line so extensively that it was declared uneconomic

Fig. 183. The abandoned viaduct at Cullingworth, near Keighley. (*Author*)

to rehabilitate. But by far the most common reason for closure was falling traffic receipts, a process which started long before the Second World War and was merely accelerated by the Beeching Report.

It is not intended to discuss the reasons for closure in great detail, but rather to concentrate on what remains, what to look for, and what is to be seen. In some cases, the track formations have been turned into footpaths, roads, and even used as the basis of a motorway. In others, the sites of old railways have disappeared altogether. Cuttings have been infilled, embankments have been removed. Stations have been turned into restaurants, industrial premises, private residences, or demolished altogether. Housing estates have sprung up across the site of the former railway. Sometimes, the remains of a railway have been totally eradicated and much was demolished during the Second World War – abandoned railway earthworks were turned into anti-tank defences when it seemed that Britain might be invaded, or destroyed during troop training exercises in the build-up to D-Day. Indeed, to this day the demolition of old bridges provides useful training for Territorial Army units.

However, much has survived. Some viaducts are listed as of historic interest and must be maintained; others would be difficult or even impossible to remove. The viaduct shown in Fig. 183 cuts cleanly through the village of Cullingworth on the Great Northern Railway's branch from Bradford to Keighley. Surrounded by houses and light industrial premises, its removal would be extremely difficult and expensive, to say nothing of the risk of damage to adjacent property. So it remains, a liability for Railtrack and its successors. The truly spectacular curved viaduct at Harecroft, only half a mile away and spanning the Harden Beck, also survives. The line was built to break the Midland's monopoly at Keighley, but the cost was high. The route was across the grain of the country, with viaducts and tunnels in quick succession. The branch from Halifax came in at Queensbury and the station was laid out as a triangle – with each of the three approaches being in tunnel! Expensive to build and expensive to operate, it succumbed to competition from the motor bus and the attentions of Dr Beeching.

The casual observer may see bridge abutments at the side of a road. Sometimes only one abutment remains, sometimes none. At Brackley, Northamptonshire, an entire viaduct was removed to make way for a bypass and, since it was built of solid concrete, demolishing it proved to be quite a task. The ends of the embankment can be seen at one side of the bypass, the A43 trunk road. At Stanks, on the northern outskirts of Leeds, one abutment over a local road remains, but the other has been partially removed to facilitate entry to a new school.

Underbridges, that is to say, road underbridges crossing a former railway, are usually infilled or removed altogether. A reduction in maintenance costs is the prime incentive for the removal of a bridge. Sometimes the opportunity is taken to straighten out a zig-zag road path over a railway bridge.

Nature, we are told, abhors straight lines. So it is reasonable to suspect the presence of an abandoned railway when confronted by an embankment with a straight and seemingly level top. A gap in the embankment where a bridge has been removed serves to confirm the matter.

A low embankment crossing a field and approaching a road at an acute angle, and a cottage where it crosses the road almost certainly indicate the site of a level crossing. Sometimes knocking on the door and asking the occupant if he or she remembers the railway may result in a rich harvest of oral history. But the occupants may be quite unaware that a track ever passed close to their home.

Tunnels present a different problem. It should be stated at the outset that, in the author's opinion, it is sheer folly to try to enter a closed railway tunnel. It might prove impossible to get out. Tunnels are sometimes maintained to guard against subsidence which would damage property above them. The entrance is usually walled up, with a door for maintenance access let into it. Occasionally the entrance is covered with earth and grassed over. Ventilation shafts are sometimes used as rubbish dumps until they are full, when the shafting above ground level is removed and the whole area grassed over.

Some earthworks are very old indeed and relate to the pre-steam age of horse-operated tramroads and plateways. For example, the course of the Brynoer tramroad can clearly be seen where it follows the contours as a ledge cut into the hillside in South Wales. At Stratford on Avon there is a bridge over the river, now used as a footpath, which originally carried the Stratford & Moreton railway.*

In a rather different category are earthworks for railways that were never completed. There are quite a number of examples, and three or four instances will suffice. The London, Brighton & South Coast Railway obtained parliamentary powers in 1864 for a track to leave the main line just south of the Ouse Valley viaduct and to strike across country in a south-easterly direction to Uckfield, and thence to join an existing line near Hailsham. It would have slightly shortened the route from London to Eastbourne, and also avoided the sharp curves and junctions at Lewes. Work started at the site of the intended main line junction, and the first 2 miles were substantially built. A shorter section west of Uckfield was also built, but a financial crisis caused the LB&SCR to abandon the works. Powers for the abandonment were obtained in an Act of 1868.

The line south from Godalming to Havant was built by a firm of contractors as a speculative venture. They hoped to sell it to the London & South Western Railway, but the company was not interested. For two or three years the line lay unused, so the developers made overtures to the South Eastern Railway, and between Shalford Junction and Peasmarsh Junction, just south of Guildford, constructed a curved embankment to join up with the South Eastern's line to Dorking and Redhill. Rather than have the South Eastern running a service to Portsmouth, the LSWR resumed negotiations and eventually purchased the line, which became known as the Portsmouth Direct line, in 1859. The curved embankment at Peasmarsh never carried a track, let alone a train.

Between Mistley and Walton on Naze, Essex, the earthworks of the Mistley, Thorpe & Walton Railway can be seen. The company ran out of funds and the time allowed for construction under the Act expired, so the line was never completed.

The viaduct over the River Wharfe at Tadcaster has quite a dramatic origin, born of railway politics. George Hudson, the so-called Railway King, was the driving force behind the York & North Midland Railway's extension from York to Leeds via Tadcaster, and construction of the viaduct at Tadcaster began in 1846. It was completed in 1849. But Hudson had gained control of the lines from Leeds to Selby, and from Selby to York, and came to regard the direct route via Tadcaster as an

---

* Still the best book for the seeker after early tramroads is Bertram Baxter's *Stone Blocks and Iron Rails* (David & Charles, 1966). Baxter was the first in the field, and his work has sins of both commission and omission, but he laid the foundation for further scholarship and his book is still invaluable as a starting point. Long out of print, it will probably have to be ordered from a second-hand book specialist, and, with the above-noted caveats, your present author wholeheartedly recommends it.

Fig. 184. The viaduct over the River Wharfe at Tadcaster, built for the direct Leeds–York railway which was never completed. (*Author*)

embarrassment. In February 1849 he expressed the hope that the line would never be completed, but the ultimate cause of the line's abandonment was the fall of the Railway King later in 1849 after an investigation showed serious financial irregularities. To this day, Tadcaster has a fine viaduct over the Wharfe which has never carried a train, apart from those on a line laid over it in 1883 to serve a corn mill on the north bank of the river.

Finally, it is often tempting to try to walk along the course of an abandoned railway, but it must be stressed that the land is in private ownership, and such a course of action is quite simply trespassing. One should always contact the owner and seek permission before attempting to follow a former railway. Quite often permission is given, but where it is not, the owner's decision should be respected.

ACKNOWLEDGEMENTS

I would like to thank all those who have made suggestions and offered help in the production of this book, in particular John Moore of York, who provided many interesting photographs – far more than I could use. John also kindly read the text in draft form and kept me 'on the right rails', so to speak. Colin Maggs also read the manuscript and saved me from at least one major error. Dieter Hopkin and David Wright of the National Railway Museum at York were especially helpful. M.R. Fairbrother and Beth Furniss made sure that I knew something about concrete sleepers, and various officers of the Permanent Way Institution came up with helpful advice. Rupert Harding and his colleagues Simon Fletcher and Sarah Moore at Sutton Publishing have performed the not inconsiderable feat of turning a manuscript into a book. The various photographers who have kindly allowed me to use their work are acknowledged individually. And finally, I would like to thank my wife Patricia, who has lived with this book for what seems a good deal longer than two years, and who has accompanied me on photographic sorties and helped with historical sources. For her unfailing patience, my grateful thanks.

I hope that I have not forgotten anyone:

David Barlow, Yorkshire Dales Railway; Arthur Elton, *British Railways*, Collins, 1945; M.R. Fairbrother, Tarmac Precast Concrete Ltd, Tallington, Stamford; Mrs Beth Furness, Tarmac Precast Concrete Ltd; Ironbridge Gorge Museum; Gavin Livie, Pandrol UK Ltd, Worksop; London Transport Museum; John Moore; Bryan Morgan, *Civil Engineering: Railways*, Longman, 1971; Dieter Hopkin, National Railway Museum, York; Miss Angela Murphy, Science Museum, London; Julian Peters, The Ivo Peters Collection; The Permanent Way Institution; Michael Poulter, British Steel Track Products, Workington; L.T.C. Rolt, *The Making of a Railway*, Wrens Park Publishing, 1999; J.N. Slinn, ISO, Historical Model Railway Society; *Railway Gazette*, various issues.

I apologise to anyone I have inadvertently omitted from the above list. I am conscious that many topics touched on here deserve extended treatment, and there are many more that I have not mentioned at all. With this caveat for omissions, all sins of commission are mine alone.

SUGGESTIONS FOR FURTHER READING

In addition to the books mentioned above, the following suggestions are offered.

Cope, Geoffrey H. (ed.), *British Railway Track* (The Permanent Way Institution, 6th Edition, 1993)

This is highly recommended to the technically minded reader.

Railway stations have not been covered by this book; there are many books available and the following are just a selection:

Antell, Robert, *Southern Country Stations: 1: London & South Western Railway*, Ian Allan, 1985
Barman, C., *Introduction to Railway Architecture* (David & Charles, 1950)
Biddle, G., *Victorian Stations* (David & Charles, 1973)
Brodribb, John, *LNER Country Stations* (Ian Allan, 1988)
Leigh, Chris, *GWR Country Stations*, 1 and 2 (Ian Allan, 1985)
Meeks, C.L.V., *The Railway Station: An Architectural History* (Yale Historical Publications, 1957)
Minnis, John, *Southern Country Stations: 2: South Eastern & Chatham Railway* (Ian Allan, 1985)

Those interested in **signalling** are directed to the following, *inter alia*:

Kitchenside, Geoffrey, and Williams, Alan, *Two Centuries of Railway Signalling* (OPC, 1998)
Pryer, G. *A Pictorial Record of Southern Signals* (Oxford Publishing Co., 1977)

And those interested in **electrification** have a wide choice. The following are recommended:

Cooper, B.K., *Electric Trains in Britain* (Ian Allan, 1979)
Moody, G.T., *Southern Electric* (Ian Allan, 1957)

INDEX